GAMES

MAGAZINE

STAR
ATTRACTIONS

STAR
ATTRACTIONS

WACKY WORDIES

SOLITAIRE HANGMAN

REBUS CARTOONS

THE FOUR-STAR PUZZLER

BY THE EDITORS OF
GAMES MAGAZINE

WORKMAN PUBLISHING, NEW YORK

Workman Publishing Company, Inc.
1 West 39 Street
New York, New York 10018

Manufactured in the United States of America
First Printing October 1986

10 9 8 7 6 5 4 3 2 1

The material in this book has previously appeared in
GAMES and THE FOUR-STAR PUZZLER,
which are trademarks of Playboy Enterprises, Inc.

ISBN: 0-89480-176-7

CONTENTS

Introduction

For the past decade, GAMES magazine has been puzzling America with a unique brand of verbal and visual challenges. The material in this book, compiled from a variety of previous GAMES publications, has been selected for its novelty and play value. The book has four parts:

Wacky Wordies are typographic rebuses that are also one of the most popular puzzles ever featured in GAMES. Each time they have appeared, readers have responded overwhelmingly by submitting their own Wacky Wordie creations, many of which appear in this book.

Solitaire Hangman, one of my own ideas, is a solitaire version of the classic word-guessing game of "hangman." By using two number charts, a player can discover whether a particular letter is in the word he or she is trying to guess—and if so, in what positions—without learning anything else about the word.

The object in **Rebus Cartoons** is to discover a name—often a celebrity, title, or place—hidden in a cartoon as a combination of its dialogue and visual elements. These challenging rebuses appeared in *The Four-Star Puzzler*, a magazine for puzzle experts published by GAMES from 1981–83.

The final chapter of this book, **The Four-Star Puzzler,** offers a selection of a wide variety of puzzles from the same source, ranging from word puzzles to logic problems to mini-mysteries.

We believe that the puzzles in this book will provide many hours of challenge and entertainment. To make sure that none of them also provide frustration, we have included all the answers in the back. Happy solving.

R. Wayne Schmittberger
Editor, GAMES Magazine

WCKY WORDIES

★☆☆☆

by the Editors
and Readers of GAMES

What's a Wacky Wordie?

In 1979, little typographic word puzzles began arriving in the GAMES mail. These "Wacky Wordies" seemed to be circulating everywhere, from hand to hand as well as by mail.

Ever alert to catch the latest wave of national frenzy before it crests, GAMES editors made up some Wacky Wordies and published a page of them. When readers sent more, GAMES published another page. And another. Over the years, GAMES has printed a few hundred of the many thousands that readers have sent in. And although each time we protest "No more" it's a good bet we'll keep on printing Wacky Wordies as long as readers continue to puzzle us with them.

The object of a Wacky Wordie is to discover the familiar word, phrase, or proper name represented by its arrangement of letters and/or symbols. The example below left illustrates the phrase "circular reasoning," and the one below right depicts "mixed bag." Both answers should give you a good idea of why Wacky Wordies are so addictively challenging.

Answers to **Wacky Wordies** start on page 368.

bopper

1

c m r e a

ban ana

2

MAN
campus

3

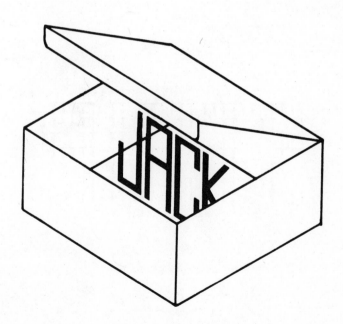

4

go off coc

5

worl

6

```
TTTT TTTTTT TTTTT  TT TTTTT
TT  TT  TT   TT  TT TT  TT   TT
TT      TT   TT  TT TT  TT   TT
  TT    TT   TTTTT  TT  TTTTT
    TT  TT   TT  TT TT  TT
TT  TT  TT   TT  TT TT  TT
  TTTT    TT   TT  TT TT  TT
```

7

8

lo head heels ve

9

you just me

10

let gone gone be gone gone

11

sight
sight
sight

love

12

13

head ache

14

✓

yearly

15

M O N I T E
O S E

16

oholene

17

world
world
world
world

18

O
V
A
T
I
O
N

19

pace **k** (crossed out)

20

breth

21

chicken

22

sesame

s d r
k i
n
house

23

24

25

L
D
Bridge

26

r
o
rail
d

27

e ^tt^ r
k   i
  c i t p

hou_{se}

28

TRN

30

bus
bus

29

c c
garage
r r

31

house
prairie

32

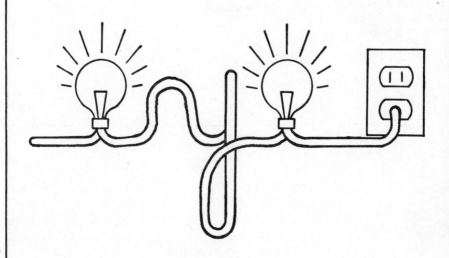

33

34

strich groound

35

morning

36

age
a g e
age

37

NINIH

38

39

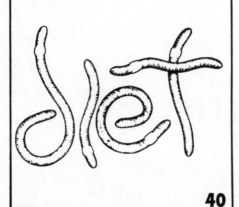

40

ping **willow**

41

V
I
O
L
E
T
s

42

43

sugar

44

milk

45

lo ose

46

47

✓ ✓ ✓
counter

48

neegr
geren
ngree
regen

49

R	R	R	R	D
O	O	O	O	N
U	U	U	U	U
N	N	N	N	O
D	D	D	D	R

ooo circus

50

dipping

51

52

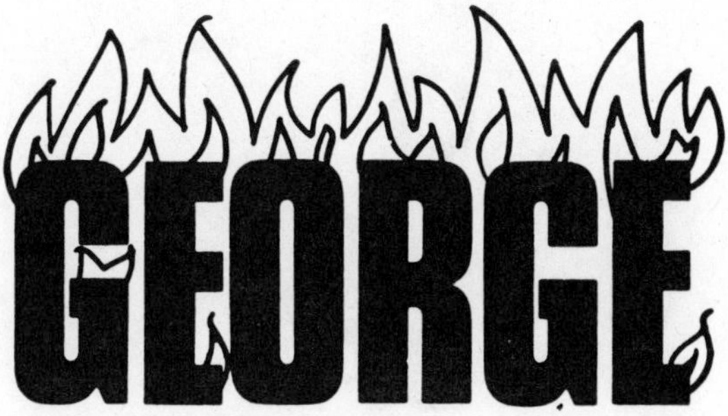
GEORGE

53

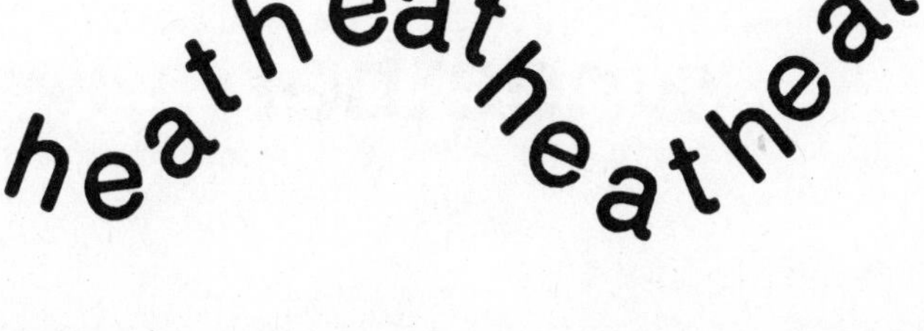
heatheatheatheat

54

O

MD

BA

PhD

55

wheather

56

cy   cy

57

clou

58

wear
long

59

momanon

60

I + T < WHOLE

61

income]

62

strokes

strokes

strokes

63

ma√il

64

budget

∧

65

C A N C E L L E D

66

inflat10n

67

shrif

68

ME ME ME
AL AL AL day

69

the market

skating
ice

70

71

law of returns

72

73

3. O
2. U
1. T

74

lu cky

75

r−i×s+k

76

77

clams
she

78

12safety345

79

i   o

t

i   n   n

a   f

l

80

HOPE

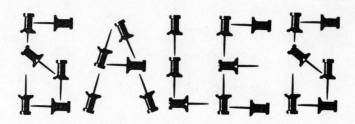

82

at the · of on

83

no ways it ways

84

TU⅄ᒷOIPᕮS

85

86

MOON SONATA

87

1.D
2.R
3.A
4.C

5.U
6.L
7.A

88

ho
ho
+ho
_____

89

T
T
+T
_____
3T

90

e

a

v

e

s

91

hand
hand
hand
deck

92

gettingitall

93

injury + insult

94

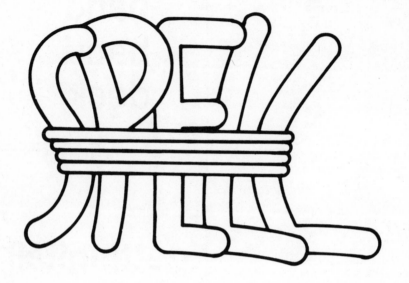

95

**g
o
s
s
i
p**

96

Symphon

97

get a word in

98

belt
hitting

99

H-O-P-E-S

100

cry
m i l k

101

SOMething

102

eyebrows

103

e e q
u a l
s m c

104

a
e   p
s   p
u   l
  a

105

to**ngue**
to**ngue**

106

night fly

107

–attitude

108

the x way

109

110

g
n
i
t da wn
t
e
g

111

1 at 3:46

112

TILL

IME

113

114

115

danc
t   e
s   c
etno

116

ieieceiie

WACKY WORDIES

wave **radio**

117

O
TV

118

noon   good

119

52

EILNPU

120

sigh

121

swear
bible
bible
bible
bible

122

g o s p e l

123

timing tim ing

124

hold

second

125

day

day

126

late n_ev_er

127

age   beauty

128

ᴗld block

129

h**a**ir___

130

socket

131

pölkä	**. that's**
132	133

SHOT

134

135

136

137

often

      not

often

      not

often

138

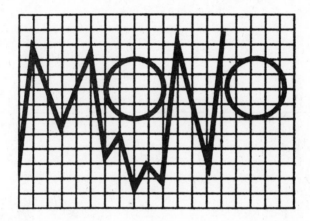

139

stereo

140

ǝlddɐǝuıd cake

141

S T I N K

142

y fireworks

143

joke

144

L V O R E E A T

145

146

TORTILLA

147

escape

148

MIRROR

149

ACCIDENT

150

participle

151

comic

152

animation

153

to earth

154

aluminum

155

search

and

156

enemy enemy

157

ri
poorch

158

**arrest
you're**

159

160

lines reading lines

161

THE PLOT

162

ca   se
case

163

a chance n

164

dothepe

165

qonpʇ

166

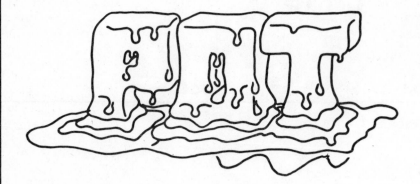

167

s
t
one

168

God
nation
✕

169

right = right

170

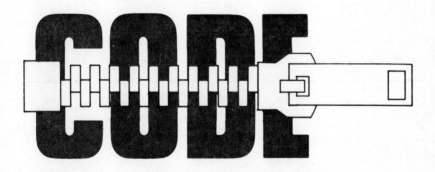

171

_{ho}**RN**

172

n^py^om^ca

173

"Duty!"

and beyond

174

my own heart a person

175

hearted

176

THUMB

177

178

harm
on
y

179

sitting
world

180

jink jink jink

181

182

¼ ¼ ¼ ¼ ¼

183

flight of

184

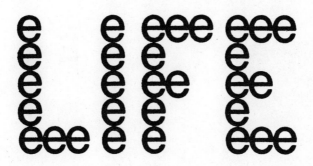

185

word YYY

186

m ce
m ce
m ce

187

B

A   E

D   U   M   R

188

189

goodbye

(displayed in an arch curve)

190

new leaf

(displayed upside down)

191

VAD ERS

Footwork

192

193

SOLITAIRE HNGMAN

★ ★ ☆ ☆

by R. Wayne Schmittberger

How to Play Solitaire Hangman

Surely most people have played Hangman at some time in their lives. It appeals both to adults and to children, not only because of its simple rules but also because it can be made as hard or as easy as required merely by choosing harder or easier words.

As in the regular two-player version of the game, the object of Solitaire Hangman is to guess the identity of a word before being "hanged." To begin, turn to the first puzzle (Body Language) and choose any letter of the alphabet that you think might belong in word I, whose length is indicated by the number of blanks following the "I." on the right-hand page. Suppose you pick E. Go to the Letter Chart on the facing (left-hand) page, and find the number listed in row E of column I (since you are working on word I). The number is 75; you now look in box number 75 in the Position Chart on the same page, and find the number 3 (just under the 75). This means that the letter E occurs in the third position, and nowhere else, in word I. If a letter occurs more than once in a word, the Position Chart will show all its locations.

If you find a 0 in the Position Chart, then that letter does not appear in the word. As a penalty for an incorrect guess, you must draw part of a stick figure below the scaffold beside the word blanks. On your first incorrect guess, draw the head; on the second the body; and on the next four, the arms and legs. If you complete the figure as shown (that is, if you make six incorrect guesses) before identifying the word, you are "hanged." Space is provided to the right of each scaffold to keep track of the letters you miss.

Word II in each puzzle is played by using column II in the Letter Chart; word III uses column III, etc.

At the end of each puzzle is a "Par Score," which represents the number of words (out of the 10 on the page) that an expert solver is likely to get right before being hanged. Since the puzzles vary in difficulty, the Par Score is a fair way of measuring your performance. (It is not an exact measure, though, since luck can play a significant part in choosing correct letters when you are just starting a puzzle.) If you equal or exceed the Par Score, you can consider yourself to have won.

This chapter contains 450 words to be guessed—and 450 chances to be hanged—arranged in 45 puzzles of 10 words each. The 20 puzzles entitled "Potpourri" are groups of miscellaneous words with nothing in common except that none are proper names. Other groups, though, are made up of words with a common theme, as suggested by their headings, and may include proper names as well as two-word names or titles.

So grab a pencil, stretch your neck, and go to it. By the time you've reached the final For Experts Only puzzle, you'll be an old hand at avoiding the hangman.

But if you do get hung up, answers to **Solitaire Hangman** start on page 370.

SOLITAIRE HANGMAN

LETTER CHART

	I	II	III	IV	V	VI	VII	VIII	IX	X
A	48	56	61	18	9	51	6	83	37	16
B	55	1	51	25	39	54	35	25	61	37
C	30	46	79	44	51	35	8	46	39	32
D	80	76	82	30	36	11	3	61	47	19
E	75	42	34	72	63	12	29	74	56	58
F	15	6	17	8	41	76	37	28	30	55
G	61	79	76	15	25	4	61	15	46	23
H	26	32	30	19	58	74	39	4	25	4
I	32	18	4	47	18	56	60	48	4	79
J	69	8	37	32	4	15	79	39	35	51
K	65	49	41	29	61	8	51	62	23	11
L	51	47	55	54	6	30	82	26	17	6
M	76	15	11	35	62	79	45	8	69	21
N	45	30	26	71	45	23	65	19	32	62
O	27	69	77	37	65	81	32	11	26	65
P	21	19	15	4	69	82	69	76	8	29
Q	79	82	21	11	79	21	41	55	11	69
R	49	67	35	51	8	55	48	35	24	64
S	82	62	65	82	35	3	17	82	76	35
T	41	55	7	55	11	19	11	66	62	76
U	4	35	19	39	82	25	4	21	79	18
V	13	21	25	61	55	32	43	30	15	82
W	8	4	32	41	15	71	15	69	29	8
X	62	25	8	62	30	37	25	32	21	15
Y	35	11	39	79	19	39	47	79	51	61
Z	11	37	43	65	21	41	55	37	82	25

	I	II	III	IV	V	VI	VII	VIII	IX	X

POSITION CHART

1	2	3	4	5
1	4, 5	3	0	1, 4
6	**7**	**8**	**9**	**10**
5	4, 7	0	3	4
11	**12**	**13**	**14**	**15**
0	8	2	2	0
16	**17**	**18**	**19**	**20**
2	1	6	0	5, 6
21	**22**	**23**	**24**	**25**
0	8	7	6	0
26	**27**	**28**	**29**	**30**
5	1	1, 7	4	0
31	**32**	**33**	**34**	**35**
5	0	6	8	0
36	**37**	**38**	**39**	**40**
4	0	5	0	2, 5
41	**42**	**43**	**44**	**45**
0	8	0	3, 7	7
46	**47**	**48**	**49**	**50**
3	0	6	4	6
51	**52**	**53**	**54**	**55**
0	1	4	5	0
56	**57**	**58**	**59**	**60**
2	7	1	5	2
61	**62**	**63**	**64**	**65**
0	0	2, 8	3	0
66	**67**	**68**	**69**	**70**
8	7	3	0	3, 8
71	**72**	**73**	**74**	**75**
1	2, 8	7	4	3
76	**77**	**78**	**79**	**80**
0	2, 3, 6	7	0	8
81	**82**	**83**	**84**	**85**
6	0	2	6	2, 7

LETTERS MISSED

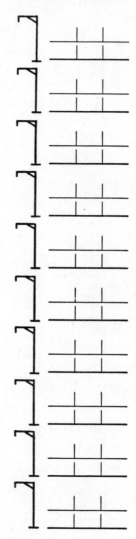

I. ___ ___ ___ ___ ___ ___ ___ ___
   1   2   3   4   5   6   7   8

II. ___ ___ ___ ___ ___ ___ ___ ___
   1   2   3   4   5   6   7   8

III. ___ ___ ___ ___ ___ ___ ___ ___
    1   2   3   4   5   6   7   8

IV. ___ ___ ___ ___ ___ ___ ___ ___
    1   2   3   4   5   6   7   8

V. ___ ___ ___ ___ ___ ___ ___ ___
   1   2   3   4   5   6   7   8

VI. ___ ___ ___ ___ ___ ___ ___ ___
    1   2   3   4   5   6   7   8

VII. ___ ___ ___ ___ ___ ___ ___
     1   2   3   4   5   6   7

VIII. ___ ___ ___ ___ ___ ___ ___ ___
      1   2   3   4   5   6   7   8

IX. ___ ___ ___ ___ ___ ___ ___
    1   2   3   4   5   6   7

X. ___ ___ ___ ___ ___ ___ ___
   1   2   3   4   5   6   7

Par Score: 7

Your Score: ____

SOLITAIRE HANGMAN

LETTER CHART

	I	II	III	IV	V	VI	VII	VIII	IX	X
A	81	70	75	30	18	14	27	28	38	9
B	78	69	21	83	75	67	65	6	65	24
C	19	14	42	59	28	31	54	81	43	67
D	14	38	24	65	14	38	67	41	47	61
E	64	51	30	67	40	21	53	18	12	14
F	49	66	38	14	34	3	69	65	45	80
G	60	74	45	31	30	60	59	45	18	60
H	34	43	60	75	41	18	74	85	2	18
I	6	84	54	16	15	68	48	23	14	3
J	8	36	71	45	74	54	31	36	21	6
K	67	24	83	49	60	69	71	69	26	21
L	5	21	6	85	36	73	5	31	6	46
M	84	67	17	15	49	5	72	49	60	69
N	18	41	16	18	38	83	36	5	46	47
O	44	4	48	81	43	10	78	10	82	73
P	47	45	41	47	26	39	60	26	74	26
Q	69	6	14	54	21	65	6	75	83	8
R	10	27	72	60	23	49	34	26	30	54
S	83	18	26	8	6	33	81	30	66	45
T	21	58	69	52	81	71	14	83	81	83
U	38	60	31	26	8	6	21	16	54	65
V	24	52	43	41	65	74	83	66	8	43
W	15	26	36	74	24	36	8	54	78	49
X	71	31	34	78	10	47	38	14	31	71
Y	31	8	65	9	31	29	47	34	49	74
Z	36	47	74	69	45	41	26	24	10	31
	I	II	III	IV	V	VI	VII	VIII	IX	X

POSITION CHART

1	2	3	4	5
1, 5	2, 5	7	4	3
6	**7**	**8**	**9**	**10**
0	7	0	2	0
11	**12**	**13**	**14**	**15**
3	4	3	0	1
16	**17**	**18**	**19**	**20**
5	3	0	4	3, 4, 7
21	**22**	**23**	**24**	**25**
0	4	6	0	6
26	**27**	**28**	**29**	**30**
0	5	2	8	7
31	**32**	**33**	**34**	**35**
0	3	1	0	7
36	**37**	**38**	**39**	**40**
0	5	0	4	3, 5
41	**42**	**43**	**44**	**45**
0	6	0	5	0
46	**47**	**48**	**49**	**50**
8	0	2	0	2
51	**52**	**53**	**54**	**55**
8	3	4, 7	0	8
56	**57**	**58**	**59**	**60**
8	5	7	6	0
61	**62**	**63**	**64**	**65**
1, 6	6	7	2, 7	0
66	**67**	**68**	**69**	**70**
1	0	2, 6	0	2
71	**72**	**73**	**74**	**75**
0	1	5	0	4
76	**77**	**78**	**79**	**80**
2	1	0	1	3, 4
81	**82**	**83**	**84**	**85**
0	3, 6	0	6	8

LETTERS MISSED

I. $\overline{\quad}\ \overline{\quad}\ \overline{\quad}\ \overline{\quad}\ \overline{\quad}\ \overline{\quad}\ \overline{\quad}$
   1   2   3   4   5   6   7

II. $\overline{\quad}\ \overline{\quad}\ \overline{\quad}\ \overline{\quad}\ \overline{\quad}\ \overline{\quad}\ \overline{\quad}\ \overline{\quad}$
   1   2   3   4   5   6   7   8

III. $\overline{\quad}\ \overline{\quad}\ \overline{\quad}\ \overline{\quad}\ \overline{\quad}\ \overline{\quad}\ \overline{\quad}$
   1   2   3   4   5   6   7

IV. $\overline{\quad}\ \overline{\quad}\ \overline{\quad}\ \overline{\quad}\ \overline{\quad}\ \overline{\quad}\ \overline{\quad}\ \overline{\quad}$
   1   2   3   4   5   6   7   8

V. $\overline{\quad}\ \overline{\quad}\ \overline{\quad}\ \overline{\quad}\ \overline{\quad}\ \overline{\quad}\ \overline{\quad}$
   1   2   3   4   5   6   7

VI. $\overline{\quad}\ \overline{\quad}\ \overline{\quad}\ \overline{\quad}\ \overline{\quad}\ \overline{\quad}\ \overline{\quad}\ \overline{\quad}$
   1   2   3   4   5   6   7   8

VII. $\overline{\quad}\ \overline{\quad}\ \overline{\quad}\ \overline{\quad}\ \overline{\quad}\ \overline{\quad}\ \overline{\quad}$
   1   2   3   4   5   6   7

VIII. $\overline{\quad}\ \overline{\quad}\ \overline{\quad}\ \overline{\quad}\ \overline{\quad}\ \overline{\quad}\ \overline{\quad}\ \overline{\quad}$
   1   2   3   4   5   6   7   8

IX. $\overline{\quad}\ \overline{\quad}\ \overline{\quad}\ \overline{\quad}\ \overline{\quad}\ \overline{\quad}\ \overline{\quad}\ \overline{\quad}$
   1   2   3   4   5   6   7   8

X. $\overline{\quad}\ \overline{\quad}\ \overline{\quad}\ \overline{\quad}\ \overline{\quad}\ \overline{\quad}\ \overline{\quad}\ \overline{\quad}$
   1   2   3   4   5   6   7   8

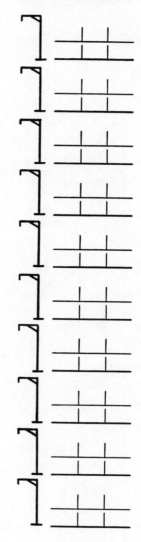

Par Score: 6

Your Score: _____

SOLITAIRE HANGMAN

LETTER CHART

	I	II	III	IV	V	VI	VII	VIII	IX	X
A	64	52	35	68	16	46	43	5	37	27
B	10	40	15	3	20	8	13	79	60	37
C	18	15	5	64	77	68	76	40	5	20
D	71	63	18	11	79	71	52	18	83	76
E	2	46	30	74	34	52	60	76	41	12
F	44	18	8	62	21	44	5	64	35	40
G	21	79	60	52	5	6	62	52	11	34
H	5	82	55	55	82	73	46	68	79	35
I	28	68	52	76	11	41	56	47	18	6
J	26	5	62	8	55	35	64	57	52	44
K	52	8	37	79	23	5	15	2	34	68
L	46	11	21	29	46	12	37	70	26	52
M	34	73	57	82	29	3	44	8	64	82
N	55	55	24	60	52	55	18	27	68	2
O	57	39	79	67	80	76	73	55	53	21
P	73	57	64	26	13	57	71	20	70	55
Q	29	13	11	57	35	62	68	34	8	18
R	74	42	66	46	26	27	55	62	45	57
S	13	21	40	5	8	13	57	11	67	5
T	40	62	44	70	81	11	65	26	15	11
U	16	34	26	13	75	82	79	73	4	26
V	35	70	46	73	37	15	29	13	29	70
W	37	77	13	2	15	64	42	82	82	8
X	15	26	29	40	57	79	8	15	13	62
Y	79	29	82	15	40	70	11	44	21	50
Z	62	64	34	44	64	18	70	21	73	64

	I	II	III	IV	V	VI	VII	VIII	IX	X

POSITION CHART

1	2	3	4	5
6	4	1	6	0
6	**7**	**8**	**9**	**10**
5	4	0	4, 7	1, 5
11	**12**	**13**	**14**	**15**
0	7	0	8	0
16	**17**	**18**	**19**	**20**
3	1, 3, 8	0	8	1
21	**22**	**23**	**24**	**25**
0	1	5	9	1
26	**27**	**28**	**29**	**30**
0	3	6	0	1, 3, 7, 8
31	**32**	**33**	**34**	**35**
5	3	3	0	0
36	**37**	**38**	**39**	**40**
7	0	5	5, 6	0
41	**42**	**43**	**44**	**45**
4	1	7	0	1
46	**47**	**48**	**49**	**50**
2	2, 5	2	3, 8	2
51	**52**	**53**	**54**	**55**
2, 3	0	2	6, 7	0
56	**57**	**58**	**59**	**60**
3	0	1, 2	4, 9	5
61	**62**	**63**	**64**	**65**
4	0	3, 7	0	4
66	**67**	**68**	**69**	**70**
4, 6	3	0	5	0
71	**72**	**73**	**74**	**75**
8	2	0	7	7
76	**77**	**78**	**79**	**80**
6	4	2	0	6
81	**82**	**83**	**84**	**85**
8	0	7	1, 8	6

LETTERS MISSED

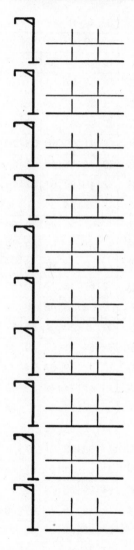

I. $\overline{\underset{1}{}\ \underset{2}{}\ \underset{3}{}\ \underset{4}{}\ \underset{5}{}\ \underset{6}{}\ \underset{7}{}\ \underset{8}{}}$

I. 1 2 3 4 5 6 7 8

II. 1 2 3 4 5 6 7

III. 1 2 3 4 5 6 7 8 9

IV. 1 2 3 4 5 6 7

V. 1 2 3 4 5 6 7 8

VI. 1 2 3 4 5 6 7 8

VII. 1 2 3 4 5 6 7 8

VIII. 1 2 3 4 5 6

IX. 1 2 3 4 5 6 7

X. 1 2 3 4 5 6 7

Par Score: 8

Your Score: _____

SOLITAIRE HANGMAN

LETTER CHART

	I	II	III	IV	V	VI	VII	VIII	IX	X
A	85	49	68	12	19	13	71	17	50	79
B	78	72	31	5	65	67	65	5	65	24
C	16	12	27	51	21	29	80	44	45	67
D	14	39	24	39	16	78	12	60	39	44
E	29	50	21	66	80	21	25	36	17	17
F	65	41	39	16	35	76	67	65	51	32
G	60	74	45	49	31	61	45	45	16	60
H	32	45	60	61	27	16	41	67	76	19
I	5	5	54	34	5	51	53	7	19	5
J	8	51	72	45	74	54	27	24	12	10
K	67	37	5	54	69	19	72	80	27	12
L	72	21	8	84	39	70	74	29	5	35
M	12	67	16	19	79	65	63	59	28	72
N	1	35	18	42	49	44	35	74	9	51
O	39	8	30	8	58	17	78	12	25	71
P	51	54	41	60	29	32	60	39	70	36
Q	74	16	19	67	24	60	5	76	78	8
R	19	47	74	72	32	55	76	55	81	58
S	6	31	29	21	2	24	8	27	37	45
T	84	22	76	55	8	80	16	8	21	16
U	41	60	32	27	17	1	19	16	54	65
V	21	65	51	41	67	74	84	49	24	54
W	24	24	65	74	12	35	54	51	72	74
X	76	19	35	76	41	39	39	19	32	76
Y	34	27	67	24	45	41	51	32	55	52
Z	27	76	84	78	51	45	29	35	8	39

	I	II	III	IV	V	VI	VII	VIII	IX	X

POSITION CHART

1	2	3	4	5
3	4	8	6, 8	0
6	**7**	**8**	**9**	**10**
5	6	0	10	1
11	**12**	**13**	**14**	**15**
3	0	6	1	9
16	**17**	**18**	**19**	**20**
0	2	3, 5	0	3
21	**22**	**23**	**24**	**25**
0	2, 5	2	0	9
26	**27**	**28**	**29**	**30**
2	0	6	0	2
31	**32**	**33**	**34**	**35**
1	0	2	2, 7	0
36	**37**	**38**	**39**	**40**
4	8	6	0	4
41	**42**	**43**	**44**	**45**
0	1, 8	2	7	0
46	**47**	**48**	**49**	**50**
7	4, 6	8	3	7
51	**52**	**53**	**54**	**55**
0	8	2, 5, 7	0	5
56	**57**	**58**	**59**	**60**
8	5	6	1	0
61	**62**	**63**	**64**	**65**
4	5	1, 4	5	0
66	**67**	**68**	**69**	**70**
9	0	4, 7	7	1
71	**72**	**73**	**74**	**75**
3	0	3	0	9
76	**77**	**78**	**79**	**80**
0	7	0	5	8
81	**82**	**83**	**84**	**85**
3, 4	3, 7, 8	1, 8	6	4

LETTERS MISSED

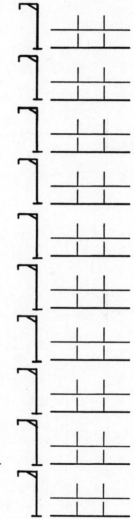

I. $\underline{\quad}\ \underline{\quad}\ \underline{\quad}\ \underline{\quad}\ \underline{\quad}\ \underline{\quad}\ \underline{\quad}$
 1 2 3 4 5 6 7

II. $\underline{\quad}\ \underline{\quad}\ \underline{\quad}\ \underline{\quad}\ \underline{\quad}\ \underline{\quad}\ \underline{\quad}\ \underline{\quad}$
 1 2 3 4 5 6 7 8

III. $\underline{\quad}\ \underline{\quad}\ \underline{\quad}\ \underline{\quad}\ \underline{\quad}\ \underline{\quad}\ \underline{\quad}$
 1 2 3 4 5 6 7

IV. $\underline{\quad}\ \underline{\quad}\ \underline{\quad}\ \underline{\quad}\ \underline{\quad}\ \underline{\quad}\ \underline{\quad}\ \underline{\quad}\ \underline{\quad}$
 1 2 3 4 5 6 7 8 9

V. $\underline{\quad}\ \underline{\quad}\ \underline{\quad}\ \underline{\quad}\ \underline{\quad}\ \underline{\quad}\ \underline{\quad}\ \underline{\quad}$
 1 2 3 4 5 6 7 8

VI. $\underline{\quad}\ \underline{\quad}\ \underline{\quad}\ \underline{\quad}\ \underline{\quad}\ \underline{\quad}\ \underline{\quad}\ \underline{\quad}$
 1 2 3 4 5 6 7 8

VII. $\underline{\quad}\ \underline{\quad}\ \underline{\quad}\ \underline{\quad}\ \underline{\quad}\ \underline{\quad}\ \underline{\quad}\ \underline{\quad}\ \underline{\quad}$
 1 2 3 4 5 6 7 8 9

VIII. $\underline{\quad}\ \underline{\quad}\ \underline{\quad}\ \underline{\quad}\ \underline{\quad}\ \underline{\quad}\ \underline{\quad}\ \underline{\quad}$
 1 2 3 4 5 6 7 8

IX. $\underline{\quad}\ \underline{\quad}\ \underline{\quad}\ \underline{\quad}\ \underline{\quad}\ \underline{\quad}\ \underline{\quad}\ \underline{\quad}\ \underline{\quad}\ \underline{\quad}$
 1 2 3 4 5 6 7 8 9 10

X. $\underline{\quad}\ \underline{\quad}\ \underline{\quad}\ \underline{\quad}\ \underline{\quad}\ \underline{\quad}\ \underline{\quad}\ \underline{\quad}$
 1 2 3 4 5 6 7 8

Par Score: 8

Your Score: _____

SOLITAIRE HANGMAN

LETTER CHART

	I	II	III	IV	V	VI	VII	VIII	IX	X
A	54	85	6	55	11	49	39	69	83	49
B	55	1	51	25	40	51	37	25	63	37
C	30	48	79	8	56	37	8	33	40	32
D	1	74	23	30	37	11	83	61	47	19
E	85	43	56	13	70	83	56	72	45	28
F	46	77	4	15	74	32	40	32	30	54
G	53	79	74	19	25	4	61	15	21	15
H	43	32	30	21	61	55	58	4	25	4
I	5	61	81	47	5	43	65	47	4	81
J	69	8	61	29	65	15	77	40	37	51
K	65	47	43	32	30	8	49	65	8	11
L	51	64	53	51	64	30	79	29	15	61
M	61	15	62	37	69	71	30	8	69	65
N	50	33	15	69	43	35	69	19	32	69
O	19	6	55	40	77	82	32	11	15	74
P	15	19	77	17	59	77	74	77	19	21
Q	74	83	21	4	79	21	43	55	6	77
R	47	69	46	39	8	61	36	1	56	35
S	83	65	65	83	33	5	26	79	5	58
T	45	53	8	49	15	19	11	57	53	79
U	4	37	19	31	83	25	4	21	39	16
V	8	21	11	61	51	74	47	83	43	8
W	77	4	25	43	19	40	15	30	49	25
X	37	25	83	65	4	47	25	74	51	30
Y	40	23	32	23	21	53	45	37	61	40
Z	79	11	37	53	32	65	55	43	55	43
	I	II	III	IV	V	VI	VII	VIII	IX	X

POSITION CHART

1	2	3	4	5
1	5, 8	3	0	4
6	**7**	**8**	**9**	**10**
5	2, 7	0	3	4
11	**12**	**13**	**14**	**15**
0	8	2	2	0
16	**17**	**18**	**19**	**20**
2	1	6	0	1, 3
21	**22**	**23**	**24**	**25**
0	8	7	6	0
26	**27**	**28**	**29**	**30**
5	1	4, 8	4	0
31	**32**	**33**	**34**	**35**
5	0	6	8	3, 7
36	**37**	**38**	**39**	**40**
4	0	5	3, 6	0
41	**42**	**43**	**44**	**45**
6, 7	8	0	3, 6	7
46	**47**	**48**	**49**	**50**
3	0	4	0	6
51	**52**	**53**	**54**	**55**
0	4	0	5	0
56	**57**	**58**	**59**	**60**
2	7	1	5	2
61	**62**	**63**	**64**	**65**
0	1, 4	1	3	0
66	**67**	**68**	**69**	**70**
8	7	3	0	1, 7
71	**72**	**73**	**74**	**75**
1	2, 3, 5	7	0	3
76	**77**	**78**	**79**	**80**
1, 6	0	7	0	8
81	**82**	**83**	**84**	**85**
6	2, 5, 6	0	6	2

LETTERS MISSED

I. __ __ __ __ __ __ __
   1   2   3   4   5   6   7

II. __ __ __ __ __ __ __
   1   2   3   4   5   6   7

III. __ __ __ __ __ __ __
   1   2   3   4   5   6   7

IV. __ __ __ __ __ __ __
   1   2   3   4   5   6   7

V. __ __ __ __ __ __ __
   1   2   3   4   5   6   7

VI. __ __ __ __ __ __ __
   1   2   3   4   5   6   7

VII. __ __ __ __ __ __ __
   1   2   3   4   5   6   7

VIII. __ __ __ __ __ __ __
    1   2   3   4   5   6   7

IX. __ __ __ __ __ __ __
   1   2   3   4   5   6   7

X. __ __ __ __ __ __ __ __
   1   2   3   4   5   6   7   8

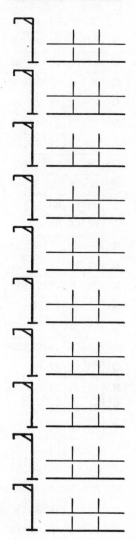

Par Score: **7**

Your Score: ____

SOLITAIRE HANGMAN

LETTER CHART

	I	II	III	IV	V	VI	VII	VIII	IX	X
A	53	12	64	73	3	79	9	37	4	57
B	44	83	28	5	39	31	49	65	52	71
C	2	46	57	28	5	42	22	34	61	72
D	27	31	81	76	69	15	28	52	9	48
E	81	73	21	44	6	14	70	67	49	22
F	31	54	31	49	59	22	42	76	20	67
G	28	22	13	72	67	9	27	81	48	35
H	15	26	5	9	44	61	15	77	81	49
I	36	65	62	11	81	44	34	84	33	24
J	76	59	35	59	18	35	11	69	46	54
K	69	28	9	67	24	33	5	11	54	5
L	58	24	73	22	21	67	65	31	21	28
M	35	9	42	24	11	24	24	44	62	9
N	34	16	77	52	72	46	82	83	34	81
O	65	5	11	34	65	37	59	71	17	31
P	42	71	39	21	28	71	39	5	83	37
Q	9	11	37	81	31	49	31	56	42	42
R	73	61	22	55	83	73	44	27	22	7
S	37	84	83	50	9	52	35	21	35	83
T	22	78	65	42	54	17	46	38	5	76
U	83	81	76	31	38	56	84	35	24	43
V	54	52	44	46	61	59	52	28	11	44
W	67	76	24	48	22	11	13	9	37	11
X	46	15	46	83	35	28	54	13	44	13
Y	72	13	49	13	48	13	61	15	13	56
Z	5	49	52	15	37	54	37	22	65	66

I II III IV V VI VII VIII IX X

POSITION CHART

1	2	3	4	5
5, 8	1	6	3	0

6	7	8	9	10
4	6	3	0	3

11	12	13	14	15
0	4, 6	0	6, 7	0

16	17	18	19	20
7	8	5	3	1

21	22	23	24	25
2	0	1, 4, 7	0	8

26	27	28	29	30
2	4	0	1, 8	8

31	32	33	34	35
0	4	5	6	0

36	37	38	39	40
5	0	3	1	6

41	42	43	44	45
5	0	2	0	4

46	47	48	49	50
0	1	7	0	1

51	52	53	54	55
7	0	2, 7	0	4, 5

56	57	58	59	60
0	5	8	0	3, 5

61	62	63	64	65
0	4	2	6	0

66	67	68	69	70
3, 4	0	2	0	2

71	72	73	74	75
1	0	3	2, 4, 6	4

76	77	78	79	80
0	7	8	2, 4	6

81	82	83	84	85
0	3, 7	0	5	7

LETTERS MISSED

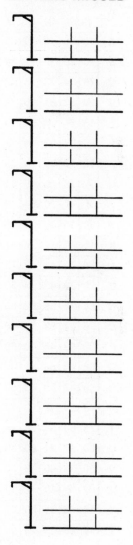

I. $\overline{}\ \overline{}\ \overline{}\ \overline{}\ \overline{}\ \overline{}\ \overline{}\ \overline{}$
   1   2   3   4   5   6   7   8

II. 1 2 3 4 5 6 7 8

III. 1 2 3 4 5 6 7

IV. 1 2 3 4 5 6 7

V. 1 2 3 4 5 6 7

VI. 1 2 3 4 5 6 7 8

VII. 1 2 3 4 5 6 7

VIII. 1 2 3 4 5 6 7

IX. 1 2 3 4 5 6 7 8

X. 1 2 3 4 5 6 7

Par Score: 8

Your Score: _____

SOLITAIRE HANGMAN

LETTER CHART

	I	II	III	IV	V	VI	VII	VIII	IX	X
A	73	55	40	19	36	24	82	26	57	44
B	20	29	5	72	34	39	28	83	20	61
C	78	14	73	78	2	43	63	46	39	2
D	26	83	81	15	5	8	69	63	75	23
E	13	74	4	35	25	68	1	44	85	68
F	5	34	23	46	9	78	68	68	46	29
G	55	17	78	80	39	60	26	48	31	73
H	4	78	48	48	51	34	55	58	34	78
I	3	5	80	64	43	63	36	5	2	15
J	80	36	39	50	46	80	43	50	78	8
K	15	46	50	5	48	9	2	2	80	34
L	34	63	41	9	72	26	78	10	60	80
M	29	39	43	34	50	15	34	8	29	36
N	66	12	55	82	55	10	58	15	50	83
O	36	84	83	2	80	37	73	20	55	75
P	39	68	46	10	58	20	39	24	26	20
Q	58	43	68	43	60	29	48	55	63	39
R	19	47	82	83	54	62	37	82	24	57
S	43	51	2	20	64	83	15	43	58	5
T	75	58	58	36	8	47	47	65	5	58
U	60	27	21	60	10	73	60	60	8	43
V	63	8	60	18	68	36	20	73	68	84
W	8	2	10	8	15	64	24	29	64	10
X	46	73	34	29	20	55	5	23	73	46
Y	10	48	63	73	63	46	80	78	48	29
Z	48	50	8	26	73	48	46	34	83	50

	I	II	III	IV	V	VI	VII	VIII	IX	X

POSITION CHART

1	2	3	4	5
4, 7	0	1, 6	3	0
6	**7**	**8**	**9**	**10**
6	3, 6	0	7	0
11	**12**	**13**	**14**	**15**
3	6	4	2	0
16	**17**	**18**	**19**	**20**
2	7	3	5	0
21	**22**	**23**	**24**	**25**
7	5	6	1	2, 5
26	**27**	**28**	**29**	**30**
0	5	6	0	7
31	**32**	**33**	**34**	**35**
3	4	7	0	1, 8
36	**37**	**38**	**39**	**40**
0	5	5	0	4
41	**42**	**43**	**44**	**45**
8	8	0	3, 5	6
46	**47**	**48**	**49**	**50**
0	3	0	1, 7	0
51	**52**	**53**	**54**	**55**
1	5	1	3	0
56	**57**	**58**	**59**	**60**
2, 4	2	0	2	0
61	**62**	**63**	**64**	**65**
1	2, 6	0	4	4, 7
66	**67**	**68**	**69**	**70**
2	1	0	8	8
71	**72**	**73**	**74**	**75**
4	6	0	8	7
76	**77**	**78**	**79**	**80**
1	8	0	6, 8	0
81	**82**	**83**	**84**	**85**
1, 5	2	0	4	5, 6

LETTERS MISSED

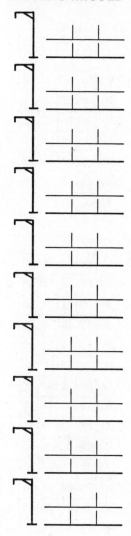

I. ___ ___ ___ ___ ___ ___ ___
    1   2   3   4   5   6   7

II. ___ ___ ___ ___ ___ ___ ___ ___
    1   2   3   4   5   6   7   8

III. ___ ___ ___ ___ ___ ___ ___ ___
    1   2   3   4   5   6   7   8

IV. ___ ___ ___ ___ ___ ___ ___ ___
    1   2   3   4   5   6   7   8

V. ___ ___ ___ ___ ___ ___ ___
    1   2   3   4   5   6   7

VI. ___ ___ ___ ___ ___ ___ ___
    1   2   3   4   5   6   7

VII. ___ ___ ___ ___ ___ ___ ___ ___
    1   2   3   4   5   6   7   8

VIII. ___ ___ ___ ___ ___ ___ ___
    1   2   3   4   5   6   7

IX. ___ ___ ___ ___ ___ ___ ___
    1   2   3   4   5   6   7

X. ___ ___ ___ ___ ___ ___ ___
    1   2   3   4   5   6   7

Par Score: 8

Your Score: ___

SOLITAIRE HANGMAN

LETTER CHART

	I	II	III	IV	V	VI	VII	VIII	IX	X
A	16	19	42	11	74	45	63	19	59	27
B	14	44	13	19	76	42	71	44	67	73
C	55	23	9	63	14	32	76	67	34	19
D	40	67	33	17	57	49	13	27	76	64
E	76	36	3	42	29	35	1	52	52	28
F	1	27	67	52	44	16	35	76	79	67
G	46	32	35	23	40	63	61	65	19	52
H	42	78	40	40	12	24	36	77	47	42
I	2	17	38	44	32	55	17	40	84	21
J	21	2	65	67	71	40	27	21	55	13
K	52	9	63	13	63	57	65	83	63	55
L	69	71	19	6	35	65	16	39	83	35
M	57	18	76	46	13	46	67	13	71	23
N	63	74	27	16	58	52	59	73	21	40
O	15	40	54	60	79	69	32	22	27	9
P	44	11	21	35	83	79	40	2	13	44
Q	9	35	2	83	9	83	19	63	2	16
R	65	76	47	36	46	70	74	32	57	71
S	19	15	44	55	52	27	79	55	23	83
T	67	42	70	71	65	47	9	74	69	46
U	12	13	46	65	19	67	83	30	65	26
V	71	79	23	57	55	44	42	35	32	57
W	74	83	71	74	21	76	64	23	7	63
X	32	21	32	21	2	19	44	42	35	2
Y	79	46	52	9	4	71	2	79	44	65
Z	13	52	74	32	67	2	21	46	74	32
	I	II	III	IV	V	VI	VII	VIII	IX	X

POSITION CHART

1	2	3	4	5
3, 4	0	2	4	6
6	**7**	**8**	**9**	**10**
3	1	3	0	1,3,8
11	**12**	**13**	**14**	**15**
4	2	0	1	7
16	**17**	**18**	**19**	**20**
5	6	1, 3	0	8
21	**22**	**23**	**24**	**25**
0	2, 4	0	1	5
26	**27**	**28**	**29**	**30**
2, 4, 6	0	7	3, 5, 8	6, 8
31	**32**	**33**	**34**	**35**
8	0	1	3	0
36	**37**	**38**	**39**	**40**
2	5	6	5, 7	0
41	**42**	**43**	**44**	**45**
4, 5	0	7	0	2
46	**47**	**48**	**49**	**50**
0	4	4	8	4
51	**52**	**53**	**54**	**55**
8	0	3	5	0
56	**57**	**58**	**59**	**60**
3	0	6, 7	7	1, 7
61	**62**	**63**	**64**	**65**
8	2	0	1	0
66	**67**	**68**	**69**	**70**
7	0	5	6	3, 7
71	**72**	**73**	**74**	**75**
0	4	3	0	7
76	**77**	**78**	**79**	**80**
0	1	5	0	8
81	**82**	**83**	**84**	**85**
2	6	0	2, 5	6

LETTERS MISSED

I. _____ _____ _____ _____ _____ _____ _____
  1   2   3   4   5   6   7

II. _____ _____ _____ _____ _____ _____ _____
  1   2   3   4   5   6   7

III. _____ _____ _____ _____ _____ _____ _____
  1   2   3   4   5   6   7

IV. _____ _____ _____ _____ _____ _____ _____
  1   2   3   4   5   6   7

V. _____ _____ _____ _____ _____ _____ _____
  1   2   3   4   5   6   7   8

VI. _____ _____ _____ _____ _____ _____ _____
  1   2   3   4   5   6   7   8

VII. _____ _____ _____ _____ _____ _____ _____
  1   2   3   4   5   6   7   8

VIII. _____ _____ _____ _____ _____ _____ _____
  1   2   3   4   5   6   7   8

IX. _____ _____ _____ _____ _____ _____ _____
  1   2   3   4   5   6   7

X. _____ _____ _____ _____ _____ _____ _____
  1   2   3   4   5   6   7

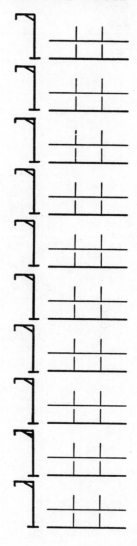

Par Score: 7

Your Score: ____

SOLITAIRE HANGMAN

LETTER CHART

	I	II	III	IV	V	VI	VII	VIII	IX	X
A	26	31	38	34	47	27	43	76	54	47
B	51	18	32	78	15	18	72	58	56	43
C	28	47	3	62	34	64	78	29	33	51
D	72	33	67	40	83	44	83	78	51	44
E	53	27	29	67	32	62	81	62	15	78
F	77	72	47	31	6	33	18	83	68	54
G	40	3	15	64	67	32	12	33	3	62
H	29	60	43	15	12	26	44	5	53	72
I	78	82	62	42	72	78	2	44	43	14
J	35	43	31	83	3	72	62	8	78	64
K	6	51	44	33	18	51	35	12	18	70
L	52	54	57	9	26	74	40	51	72	31
M	3	74	6	18	20	40	6	15	62	69
N	31	40	61	3	14	34	45	64	29	81
O	12	12	82	32	76	45	4	6	84	12
P	43	29	64	35	22	8	67	18	31	50
Q	83	35	18	43	8	20	22	54	67	15
R	42	48	72	22	29	3	51	31	20	56
S	8	62	40	30	40	29	33	3	25	29
T	33	5	12	44	31	67	8	10	52	67
U	81	44	74	6	43	6	74	14	35	61
V	44	78	83	8	5	31	15	74	83	22
W	47	56	5	12	33	12	20	20	74	3
X	54	64	20	47	35	35	64	35	64	83
Y	20	67	51	14	52	52	29	43	22	33
Z	56	6	33	20	44	43	46	22	6	74
	I	II	III	IV	V	VI	VII	VIII	IX	X

POSITION CHART

1	2	3	4	5
8	2, 5	0	3	4

6	7	8	9	10
0	8	0	4, 8	3, 5

11	12	13	14	15
2	0	2	6	0

16	17	18	19	20
2	4	0	1, 7, 8	0

21	22	23	24	25
4	0	7	6	4

26	27	28	29	30
3	2, 6	4	0	3

31	32	33	34	35
0	5	0	7	0

36	37	38	39	40
7	5	6	7	1

41	42	43	44	45
1	2	0	0	4

46	47	48	49	50
6	0	7	1	1, 4

51	52	53	54	55
0	8	5	0	5

56	57	58	59	60
0	7, 8	1, 7	8	5

61	62	63	64	65
2	0	4, 5	0	6

66	67	68	69	70
3, 6	0	2, 3	3	5

71	72	73	74	75
8	0	3	0	1

76	77	78	79	80
2	6	0	1	1

81	82	83	84	85
7	3	0	1, 6, 7	8

LETTERS MISSED

I. $\overline{}$
1 2 3 4 5 6 7 8

II. $\overline{}$
1 2 3 4 5 6 7

III. $\overline{}$
1 2 3 4 5 6 7 8

IV. $\overline{}$
1 2 3 4 5 6 7 8

V. $\overline{}$
1 2 3 4 5 6 7 8

VI. $\overline{}$
1 2 3 4 5 6 7 8

VII. $\overline{}$
1 2 3 4 5 6 7

VIII. $\overline{}$
1 2 3 4 5 6 7

IX. $\overline{}$
1 2 3 4 5 6 7 8

X. $\overline{}$
1 2 3 4 5 6 7

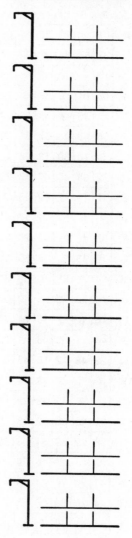

Par Score: 7

Your Score: _____

SOLITAIRE HANGMAN

LETTER CHART

	I	II	III	IV	V	VI	VII	VIII	IX	X
A	31	8	73	35	10	66	22	60	39	22
B	33	55	84	72	32	14	10	50	18	10
C	18	43	10	43	35	58	19	19	58	65
D	68	81	26	58	3	74	84	79	35	79
E	5	36	2	23	82	29	48	57	70	28
F	65	50	48	57	51	35	33	84	51	33
G	6	70	80	73	38	12	41	53	72	74
H	72	84	40	47	18	76	45	82	29	11
I	17	19	12	62	25	7	36	3	19	3
J	7	3	57	29	57	41	62	29	10	19
K	35	12	29	41	29	28	70	48	28	7
L	19	33	22	38	30	2	79	67	64	25
M	84	76	35	3	58	51	65	33	47	29
N	79	72	79	51	12	53	3	35	76	76
O	76	6	17	16	64	72	83	1	65	16
P	48	11	7	48	41	79	72	51	79	22
Q	29	48	72	53	43	3	7	7	38	12
R	73	60	6	22	14	19	14	10	48	35
S	81	79	19	28	19	55	73	22	81	41
T	32	65	63	32	53	73	51	46	84	72
U	38	29	59	54	48	62	29	74	32	43
V	22	51	14	10	22	81	53	12	43	14
W	41	74	76	74	65	47	32	72	12	38
X	14	10	38	55	55	22	35	14	41	73
Y	43	32	32	7	72	10	74	32	3	48
Z	51	7	41	59	62	57	55	59	74	51

I II III IV V VI VII VIII IX X

POSITION CHART

1	2	3	4	5
2	6	0	1, 3	8

6	7	8	9	10
7	0	3	6	0

11	12	13	14	15
4	0	2, 4, 6	0	1

16	17	18	19	20
2, 5	2	5	0	3

21	22	23	24	25
2	0	8	5	6

26	27	28	29	30
8	5	7	0	3, 7, 8

31	32	33	34	35
6	0	1	5	0

36	37	38	39	40
2	1	0	3, 6	5

41	42	43	44	45
0	7	0	7	4, 5

46	47	48	49	50
3	0	3	3	5

51	52	53	54	55
0	7	0	6	0

56	57	58	59	60
5, 7	0	1	0	6

61	62	63	64	65
1	0	4	2	0

66	67	68	69	70
2, 5	7, 8	4	4	8

71	72	73	74	75
8	0	3	0	2

76	77	78	79	80
0	8	2, 6	0	1

81	82	83	84	85
0	4	6, 7	0	3

LETTERS MISSED

I. ___ ___ ___ ___ ___ ___ ___ ___
 1 2 3 4 5 6 7 8

II. ___ ___ ___ ___ ___ ___ ___ ___
 1 2 3 4 5 6 7 8

III. ___ ___ ___ ___ ___ ___ ___ ___
 1 2 3 4 5 6 7 8

IV. ___ ___ ___ ___ ___ ___ ___ ___
 1 2 3 4 5 6 7 8

V. ___ ___ ___ ___ ___ ___ ___ ___
 1 2 3 4 5 6 7 8

VI. ___ ___ ___ ___ ___ ___ ___
 1 2 3 4 5 6 7

VII. ___ ___ ___ ___ ___ ___ ___ ___
 1 2 3 4 5 6 7 8

VIII. ___ ___ ___ ___ ___ ___ ___ ___
 1 2 3 4 5 6 7 8

IX. ___ ___ ___ ___ ___ ___ ___ ___
 1 2 3 4 5 6 7 8

X. ___ ___ ___ ___ ___ ___ ___
 1 2 3 4 5 6 7

Par Score: 8

Your Score: _____

105

SOLITAIRE HANGMAN

LETTER CHART

	I	II	III	IV	V	VI	VII	VIII	IX	X
A	23	49	22	23	5	35	7	64	57	1
B	70	5	43	80	21	80	50	29	58	10
C	15	56	62	47	68	3	26	16	45	3
D	14	62	70	64	62	83	10	43	10	84
E	61	19	12	37	53	62	8	83	22	47
F	50	29	72	58	43	21	74	26	62	43
G	52	47	48	6	50	64	62	70	14	66
H	29	58	10	5	54	10	29	30	21	83
I	64	17	26	52	27	14	58	13	19	35
J	66	80	31	35	64	43	45	31	26	14
K	22	72	80	83	69	5	70	5	64	21
L	43	21	28	70	26	45	11	10	2	74
M	47	12	5	10	29	26	3	66	35	5
N	4	73	63	76	37	63	76	37	65	76
O	5	84	29	14	14	23	20	58	79	51
P	12	50	39	66	83	85	52	35	9	70
Q	19	26	14	45	47	19	64	72	29	19
R	74	81	35	19	10	22	35	14	83	26
S	21	43	58	68	31	29	14	47	43	50
T	58	31	17	26	35	66	56	21	31	29
U	45	66	45	71	19	31	43	82	52	31
V	26	45	66	50	45	47	31	45	47	18
W	62	83	74	21	72	50	47	19	5	45
X	72	52	47	72	52	58	5	74	50	80
Y	31	64	76	62	58	52	66	50	66	52
Z	76	35	83	43	66	70	72	12	70	58

	I	II	III	IV	V	VI	VII	VIII	IX	X

POSITION CHART

1	2	3	4	5
1, 5	5	4	3	0
6	**7**	**8**	**9**	**10**
6	2, 6	5	3	0
11	**12**	**13**	**14**	**15**
7	1	6, 8	0	4
16	**17**	**18**	**19**	**20**
3, 4	8	2	0	1
21	**22**	**23**	**24**	**25**
0	6	2, 5	8	4
26	**27**	**28**	**29**	**30**
0	3	5	0	5
31	**32**	**33**	**34**	**35**
0	1	8	1	0
36	**37**	**38**	**39**	**40**
1	7	1, 4	4	8
41	**42**	**43**	**44**	**45**
8	2	0	6	0
46	**47**	**48**	**49**	**50**
6	0	2, 3	2, 4	0
51	**52**	**53**	**54**	**55**
3, 7	0	6	2	4
56	**57**	**58**	**59**	**60**
3	2	0	4	1
61	**62**	**63**	**64**	**65**
7	0	7	0	1, 8
66	**67**	**68**	**69**	**70**
0	2	1, 4	5	0
71	**72**	**73**	**74**	**75**
3	0	7	0	1, 7
76	**77**	**78**	**79**	**80**
0	3	7	4, 7	0
81	**82**	**83**	**84**	**85**
5	2	0	6	1, 3

LETTERS MISSED

I. $\dfrac{\quad}{1} \dfrac{\quad}{2} \dfrac{\quad}{3} \dfrac{\quad}{4} \dfrac{\quad}{5} \dfrac{\quad}{6} \dfrac{\quad}{7}$

II. $\dfrac{\quad}{1} \dfrac{\quad}{2} \dfrac{\quad}{3} \dfrac{\quad}{4} \dfrac{\quad}{5} \dfrac{\quad}{6} \dfrac{\quad}{7} \dfrac{\quad}{8}$

III. $\dfrac{\quad}{1} \dfrac{\quad}{2} \dfrac{\quad}{3} \dfrac{\quad}{4} \dfrac{\quad}{5} \dfrac{\quad}{6} \dfrac{\quad}{7} \dfrac{\quad}{8}$

IV. $\dfrac{\quad}{1} \dfrac{\quad}{2} \dfrac{\quad}{3} \dfrac{\quad}{4} \dfrac{\quad}{5} \dfrac{\quad}{6} \dfrac{\quad}{7}$

V. $\dfrac{\quad}{1} \dfrac{\quad}{2} \dfrac{\quad}{3} \dfrac{\quad}{4} \dfrac{\quad}{5} \dfrac{\quad}{6} \dfrac{\quad}{7}$

VI. $\dfrac{\quad}{1} \dfrac{\quad}{2} \dfrac{\quad}{3} \dfrac{\quad}{4} \dfrac{\quad}{5} \dfrac{\quad}{6} \dfrac{\quad}{7}$

VII. $\dfrac{\quad}{1} \dfrac{\quad}{2} \dfrac{\quad}{3} \dfrac{\quad}{4} \dfrac{\quad}{5} \dfrac{\quad}{6} \dfrac{\quad}{7}$

VIII. $\dfrac{\quad}{1} \dfrac{\quad}{2} \dfrac{\quad}{3} \dfrac{\quad}{4} \dfrac{\quad}{5} \dfrac{\quad}{6} \dfrac{\quad}{7} \dfrac{\quad}{8}$

IX. $\dfrac{\quad}{1} \dfrac{\quad}{2} \dfrac{\quad}{3} \dfrac{\quad}{4} \dfrac{\quad}{5} \dfrac{\quad}{6} \dfrac{\quad}{7} \dfrac{\quad}{8}$

X. $\dfrac{\quad}{1} \dfrac{\quad}{2} \dfrac{\quad}{3} \dfrac{\quad}{4} \dfrac{\quad}{5} \dfrac{\quad}{6} \dfrac{\quad}{7}$

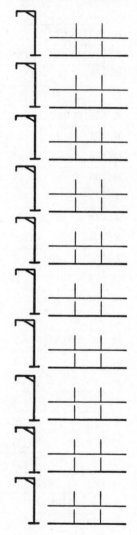

Par Score: 8

Your Score: _____

SOLITAIRE HANGMAN

LETTER CHART

	I	II	III	IV	V	VI	VII	VIII	IX	X
A	53	61	32	36	77	29	22	35	79	73
B	79	15	38	27	84	79	34	2	41	48
C	67	17	55	28	79	71	79	53	12	49
D	22	35	71	78	81	62	4	8	53	71
E	85	80	67	17	49	84	10	47	18	19
F	71	48	79	70	27	44	67	56	27	2
G	84	6	41	12	53	60	81	24	15	32
H	36	2	61	30	80	81	19	27	26	53
I	74	22	74	41	24	78	44	31	56	65
J	44	31	81	71	31	27	62	60	38	60
K	24	74	31	74	20	49	15	12	20	74
L	56	10	44	2	35	77	84	74	73	15
M	15	71	12	15	19	13	38	5	17	24
N	34	20	25	77	34	52	32	49	85	8
O	62	84	84	44	45	2	12	38	2	56
P	31	60	53	49	30	56	46	62	24	3
Q	12	27	24	56	60	4	24	20	67	79
R	19	8	20	35	74	6	60	61	31	17
S	81	64	68	20	4	22	30	30	35	31
T	30	34	36	60	65	30	45	85	61	20
U	77	62	7	85	17	15	36	41	81	35
V	2	9	2	24	8	67	2	17	34	38
W	27	53	49	31	38	8	35	15	46	27
X	4	79	15	79	2	74	41	6	49	62
Y	38	41	27	38	41	12	31	16	74	84
Z	6	56	4	62	56	17	49	46	44	81
	I	II	III	IV	V	VI	VII	VIII	IX	X

POSITION CHART

1	2	3	4	5
3	0	4, 6	0	3, 4
6	**7**	**8**	**9**	**10**
0	4	0	6	8
11	**12**	**13**	**14**	**15**
8	0	6	6	0
16	**17**	**18**	**19**	**20**
2, 8	0	1, 3, 5	7	0
21	**22**	**23**	**24**	**25**
7	5	7	0	5
26	**27**	**28**	**29**	**30**
8	0	5	2, 7	1
31	**32**	**33**	**34**	**35**
0	3	3	4	0
36	**37**	**38**	**39**	**40**
2	4	0	2, 3	2
41	**42**	**43**	**44**	**45**
0	2	4	0	6
46	**47**	**48**	**49**	**50**
0	5	1	0	3
51	**52**	**53**	**54**	**55**
4	8	0	1	6
56	**57**	**58**	**59**	**60**
0	3, 5, 6	4	4, 8	0
61	**62**	**63**	**64**	**65**
7	0	8	3	5
66	**67**	**68**	**69**	**70**
7	0	1	5	7, 8
71	**72**	**73**	**74**	**75**
0	7	2	0	2
76	**77**	**78**	**79**	**80**
1	3	4	0	2
81	**82**	**83**	**84**	**85**
0	8	1	0	6

LETTERS MISSED

I. $\underline{}$ $\underline{}$ $\underline{}$ $\underline{}$ $\underline{}$ $\underline{}$ $\underline{}$
    1   2   3   4   5   6   7

II. $\underline{}$ $\underline{}$ $\underline{}$ $\underline{}$ $\underline{}$ $\underline{}$ $\underline{}$ $\underline{}$
    1   2   3   4   5   6   7   8

III. $\underline{}$ $\underline{}$ $\underline{}$ $\underline{}$ $\underline{}$ $\underline{}$ $\underline{}$
    1   2   3   4   5   6   7

IV. $\underline{}$ $\underline{}$ $\underline{}$ $\underline{}$ $\underline{}$ $\underline{}$ $\underline{}$ $\underline{}$
    1   2   3   4   5   6   7   8

V. $\underline{}$ $\underline{}$ $\underline{}$ $\underline{}$ $\underline{}$ $\underline{}$ $\underline{}$
    1   2   3   4   5   6   7

VI. $\underline{}$ $\underline{}$ $\underline{}$ $\underline{}$ $\underline{}$ $\underline{}$ $\underline{}$ $\underline{}$
    1   2   3   4   5   6   7   8

VII. $\underline{}$ $\underline{}$ $\underline{}$ $\underline{}$ $\underline{}$ $\underline{}$ $\underline{}$ $\underline{}$
    1   2   3   4   5   6   7   8

VIII. $\underline{}$ $\underline{}$ $\underline{}$ $\underline{}$ $\underline{}$ $\underline{}$ $\underline{}$ $\underline{}$
    1   2   3   4   5   6   7   8

IX. $\underline{}$ $\underline{}$ $\underline{}$ $\underline{}$ $\underline{}$ $\underline{}$ $\underline{}$ $\underline{}$
    1   2   3   4   5   6   7   8

X. $\underline{}$ $\underline{}$ $\underline{}$ $\underline{}$ $\underline{}$ $\underline{}$ $\underline{}$
    1   2   3   4   5   6   7

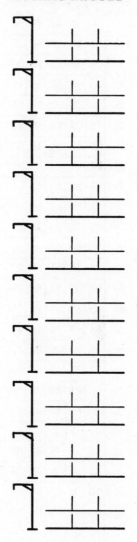

Par Score: 7

Your Score: _____

SOLITAIRE HANGMAN

LETTER CHART

	I	II	III	IV	V	VI	VII	VIII	IX	X
A	59	19	17	46	4	33	2	65	40	83
B	25	45	71	23	30	45	12	79	9	15
C	33	15	30	37	62	80	70	20	62	28
D	24	72	77	25	12	25	45	69	45	77
E	76	29	79	43	40	52	31	51	52	45
F	45	65	85	16	33	79	59	30	47	79
G	77	47	81	45	16	47	16	49	76	27
H	47	82	69	47	57	1	82	74	77	4
I	71	69	82	69	20	82	77	12	32	22
J	49	74	25	74	37	2	4	22	37	65
K	12	53	84	4	81	22	36	33	49	69
L	27	55	11	80	22	58	25	44	53	55
M	56	37	65	62	79	77	20	16	59	30
N	80	49	41	77	25	56	33	53	74	12
O	64	77	74	12	32	44	79	18	16	53
P	84	79	35	20	27	73	65	81	30	57
Q	74	81	12	22	71	30	47	45	65	2
R	53	23	33	3	39	20	63	62	82	72
S	5	60	45	58	59	57	60	77	84	16
T	37	12	2	27	42	4	49	11	55	5
U	55	33	49	81	61	69	74	56	25	20
V	57	2	4	59	65	81	79	84	20	33
W	16	84	27	84	45	49	27	55	69	47
X	30	20	16	65	47	37	30	25	27	74
Y	81	85	20	49	84	27	22	47	79	49
Z	65	59	37	79	55	53	37	85	2	81
	I	II	III	IV	V	VI	VII	VIII	IX	X

POSITION CHART

1 / 6	**2** / 0	**3** / 3	**4** / 0	**5** / 8
6 / 6	**7** / 2	**8** / 3	**9** / 4, 5	**10** / 4
11 / 6, 7	**12** / 0	**13** / 5	**14** / 6	**15** / 1
16 / 0	**17** / 5	**18** / 2	**19** / 3, 5	**20** / 0
21 / 2	**22** / 0	**23** / 4	**24** / 1	**25** / 0
26 / 5	**27** / 0	**28** / 3, 4	**29** / 7	**30** / 0
31 / 3, 6	**32** / 3	**33** / 0	**34** / 3	**35** / 1
36 / 5	**37** / 0	**38** / 7	**39** / 2	**40** / 6
41 / 3	**42** / 7	**43** / 6	**44** / 4	**45** / 0
46 / 2	**47** / 0	**48** / 4	**49** / 0	**50** / 4
51 / 5, 8	**52** / 8	**53** / 0	**54** / 8	**55** / 0
56 / 3	**57** / 0	**58** / 7	**59** / 0	**60** / 8
61 / 5	**62** / 1	**63** / 7	**64** / 2, 6	**65** / 0
66 / 2, 4	**67** / 8	**68** / 1	**69** / 0	**70** / 1, 4
71 / 4	**72** / 6	**73** / 1	**74** / 0	**75** / 1, 7
76 / 7	**77** / 0	**78** / 3, 5, 6	**79** / 0	**80** / 5
81 / 0	**82** / 2	**83** / 2, 5, 7	**84** / 0	**85** / 0

LETTERS MISSED

I. <u>   </u>
   1   2   3   4   5   6   7   8

II. <u>   </u>
   1   2   3   4   5   6   7   8

III. <u>   </u>
   1   2   3   4   5   6   7

IV. <u>   </u>
   1   2   3   4   5   6   7

V. <u>   </u>
   1   2   3   4   5   6   7

VI. <u>   </u>
   1   2   3   4   5   6   7   8

VII. <u>   </u>
   1   2   3   4   5   6   7   8

VIII. <u>   </u>
   1   2   3   4   5   6   7   8

IX. <u>   </u>
   1   2   3   4   5   6   7   8

X. <u>   </u>
   1   2   3   4   5   6   7   8

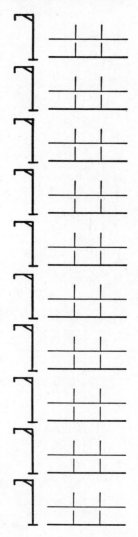

Par Score: 8

Your Score: _____

SOLITAIRE HANGMAN

LETTER CHART

	I	II	III	IV	V	VI	VII	VIII	IX	X
A	7	20	11	45	12	33	61	36	41	19
B	44	21	1	31	73	23	73	52	56	78
C	23	38	66	44	33	15	24	27	23	47
D	73	26	47	4	30	75	38	7	66	80
E	8	11	44	51	15	22	27	69	27	4
F	46	73	52	15	21	52	78	62	75	44
G	75	30	54	78	29	73	23	10	83	52
H	21	27	4	38	52	58	80	4	78	66
I	49	42	27	30	80	46	4	72	52	69
J	62	15	58	52	27	38	75	44	38	27
K	9	58	7	66	67	74	7	80	7	7
L	52	16	9	59	83	55	19	29	21	26
M	74	23	62	27	32	7	35	75	4	35
N	64	65	67	21	74	42	22	43	35	9
O	69	32	84	69	9	44	66	9	63	31
P	4	29	69	54	23	4	9	84	9	1
Q	38	47	73	62	38	54	58	66	69	21
R	33	75	5	35	59	62	47	15	29	73
S	78	44	46	33	54	66	11	22	62	5
T	11	4	3	23	7	9	52	11	59	28
U	29	7	74	58	44	11	29	73	72	75
V	47	33	29	26	47	78	15	21	33	11
W	15	78	15	73	58	10	33	2	73	15
X	27	52	75	75	4	69	62	47	11	23
Y	54	80	38	29	66	80	21	78	44	54
Z	58	9	78	47	78	21	44	23	54	29
	I	II	III	IV	V	VI	VII	VIII	IX	X

POSITION CHART

1	**2**	**3**	**4**	**5**
4, 5	1	2	0	7
6	**7**	**8**	**9**	**10**
3, 8	0	2, 8	0	4
11	**12**	**13**	**14**	**15**
0	2, 6	7	4	0
16	**17**	**18**	**19**	**20**
8	3	8	2	3, 7
21	**22**	**23**	**24**	**25**
0	5	0	7	4, 5, 7
26	**27**	**28**	**29**	**30**
1	0	8	0	4
31	**32**	**33**	**34**	**35**
6	5	0	6	3
36	**37**	**38**	**39**	**40**
7	4	0	5	3
41	**42**	**43**	**44**	**45**
6	2	3, 8	0	2, 5
46	**47**	**48**	**49**	**50**
1	0	2	4, 6	1
51	**52**	**53**	**54**	**55**
8	0	8	0	6, 7
56	**57**	**58**	**59**	**60**
4	4	0	7	5
61	**62**	**63**	**64**	**65**
1, 4, 6	0	5	5, 7	6
66	**67**	**68**	**69**	**70**
0	8	7	0	1, 8
71	**72**	**73**	**74**	**75**
6	2	0	3	0
76	**77**	**78**	**79**	**80**
3	2, 4, 7	0	3	0
81	**82**	**83**	**84**	**85**
2	5	1	6	1

LETTERS MISSED

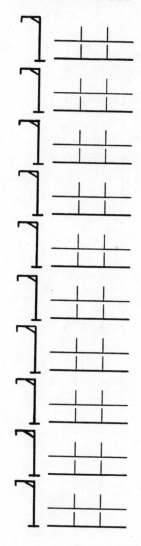

I. $\overline{}_{1}\ \overline{}_{2}\ \overline{}_{3}\ \overline{}_{4}\ \overline{}_{5}\ \overline{}_{6}\ \overline{}_{7}\ \overline{}_{8}$

II. $\overline{}_{1}\ \overline{}_{2}\ \overline{}_{3}\ \overline{}_{4}\ \overline{}_{5}\ \overline{}_{6}\ \overline{}_{7}\ \overline{}_{8}$

III. $\overline{}_{1}\ \overline{}_{2}\ \overline{}_{3}\ \overline{}_{4}\ \overline{}_{5}\ \overline{}_{6}\ \overline{}_{7}\ \overline{}_{8}$

IV. $\overline{}_{1}\ \overline{}_{2}\ \overline{}_{3}\ \overline{}_{4}\ \overline{}_{5}\ \overline{}_{6}\ \overline{}_{7}\ \overline{}_{8}$

V. $\overline{}_{1}\ \overline{}_{2}\ \overline{}_{3}\ \overline{}_{4}\ \overline{}_{5}\ \overline{}_{6}\ \overline{}_{7}\ \overline{}_{8}$

VI. $\overline{}_{1}\ \overline{}_{2}\ \overline{}_{3}\ \overline{}_{4}\ \overline{}_{5}\ \overline{}_{6}\ \overline{}_{7}$

VII. $\overline{}_{1}\ \overline{}_{2}\ \overline{}_{3}\ \overline{}_{4}\ \overline{}_{5}\ \overline{}_{6}\ \overline{}_{7}$

VIII. $\overline{}_{1}\ \overline{}_{2}\ \overline{}_{3}\ \overline{}_{4}\ \overline{}_{5}\ \overline{}_{6}\ \overline{}_{7}\ \overline{}_{8}$

IX. $\overline{}_{1}\ \overline{}_{2}\ \overline{}_{3}\ \overline{}_{4}\ \overline{}_{5}\ \overline{}_{6}\ \overline{}_{7}$

X. $\overline{}_{1}\ \overline{}_{2}\ \overline{}_{3}\ \overline{}_{4}\ \overline{}_{5}\ \overline{}_{6}\ \overline{}_{7}\ \overline{}_{8}$

Par Score: 7

Your Score: _____

SOLITAIRE HANGMAN

LETTER CHART

	I	II	III	IV	V	VI	VII	VIII	IX	X
A	52	73	70	5	16	17	70	28	76	66
B	36	81	42	33	38	73	63	8	52	44
C	28	46	17	52	17	58	45	5	66	41
D	79	52	45	66	5	76	66	83	11	11
E	66	30	24	29	12	3	58	22	84	28
F	20	31	8	17	20	78	36	11	24	52
G	3	79	69	73	42	20	78	52	69	46
H	5	54	13	69	58	12	46	31	17	14
I	12	8	47	53	24	8	81	42	20	34
J	24	28	78	46	28	36	13	13	5	5
K	11	69	11	76	66	28	31	81	28	8
L	31	66	16	42	47	81	39	34	36	58
M	69	11	71	78	6	52	69	17	59	83
N	73	35	33	1	57	11	8	20	39	69
O	71	3	28	16	59	38	29	44	44	54
P	37	13	76	36	8	27	73	24	71	10
Q	76	36	5	81	31	83	76	58	42	39
R	45	38	21	18	33	45	49	77	9	42
S	8	37	81	83	13	5	20	29	4	45
T	33	76	66	61	36	16	16	63	33	13
U	17	45	52	11	46	31	83	33	81	73
V	78	24	20	38	69	44	17	73	54	31
W	13	5	31	8	73	54	5	60	31	76
X	81	58	73	31	11	13	11	66	73	17
Y	51	33	36	58	39	33	24	36	46	71
Z	39	17	44	28	76	24	28	39	78	78
	I	II	III	IV	V	VI	VII	VIII	IX	X

POSITION CHART

1	2	3	4	5
2, 5	4	6	6, 7	0
6	**7**	**8**	**9**	**10**
6	1	0	4	1
11	**12**	**13**	**14**	**15**
0	5	0	5	1, 3, 7
16	**17**	**18**	**19**	**20**
7	0	8	7	0
21	**22**	**23**	**24**	**25**
5	3, 7	5	0	7
26	**27**	**28**	**29**	**30**
8	1, 4	0	4	5
31	**32**	**33**	**34**	**35**
0	8	0	6	7
36	**37**	**38**	**39**	**40**
0	1	3	0	3
41	**42**	**43**	**44**	**45**
4, 7	0	7	0	2
46	**47**	**48**	**49**	**50**
0	4	5, 8	3	6
51	**52**	**53**	**54**	**55**
7	0	1	0	3, 5, 7
56	**57**	**58**	**59**	**60**
4	1, 8	0	2	1
61	**62**	**63**	**64**	**65**
6	2	5	6	2
66	**67**	**68**	**69**	**70**
0	8	2	0	1, 6
71	**72**	**73**	**74**	**75**
3	8	0	1	2
76	**77**	**78**	**79**	**80**
0	2, 8	0	4	3
81	**82**	**83**	**84**	**85**
0	3	0	1, 5	8

LETTERS MISSED

I. $\overline{\quad}_1 \ \overline{\quad}_2 \ \overline{\quad}_3 \ \overline{\quad}_4 \ \overline{\quad}_5 \ \overline{\quad}_6 \ \overline{\quad}_7$

II. $\overline{\quad}_1 \ \overline{\quad}_2 \ \overline{\quad}_3 \ \overline{\quad}_4 \ \overline{\quad}_5 \ \overline{\quad}_6 \ \overline{\quad}_7$

III. $\overline{\quad}_1 \ \overline{\quad}_2 \ \overline{\quad}_3 \ \overline{\quad}_4 \ \overline{\quad}_5 \ \overline{\quad}_6 \ \overline{\quad}_7$

IV. $\overline{\quad}_1 \ \overline{\quad}_2 \ \overline{\quad}_3 \ \overline{\quad}_4 \ \overline{\quad}_5 \ \overline{\quad}_6 \ \overline{\quad}_7 \ \overline{\quad}_8$

V. $\overline{\quad}_1 \ \overline{\quad}_2 \ \overline{\quad}_3 \ \overline{\quad}_4 \ \overline{\quad}_5 \ \overline{\quad}_6 \ \overline{\quad}_7 \ \overline{\quad}_8$

VI. $\overline{\quad}_1 \ \overline{\quad}_2 \ \overline{\quad}_3 \ \overline{\quad}_4 \ \overline{\quad}_5 \ \overline{\quad}_6 \ \overline{\quad}_7$

VII. $\overline{\quad}_1 \ \overline{\quad}_2 \ \overline{\quad}_3 \ \overline{\quad}_4 \ \overline{\quad}_5 \ \overline{\quad}_6 \ \overline{\quad}_7$

VIII. $\overline{\quad}_1 \ \overline{\quad}_2 \ \overline{\quad}_3 \ \overline{\quad}_4 \ \overline{\quad}_5 \ \overline{\quad}_6 \ \overline{\quad}_7 \ \overline{\quad}_8$

IX. $\overline{\quad}_1 \ \overline{\quad}_2 \ \overline{\quad}_3 \ \overline{\quad}_4 \ \overline{\quad}_5 \ \overline{\quad}_6 \ \overline{\quad}_7$

X. $\overline{\quad}_1 \ \overline{\quad}_2 \ \overline{\quad}_3 \ \overline{\quad}_4 \ \overline{\quad}_5 \ \overline{\quad}_6 \ \overline{\quad}_7$

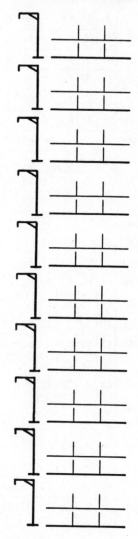

Par Score: 7

Your Score: _____

SOLITAIRE HANGMAN

LETTER CHART

	I	II	III	IV	V	VI	VII	VIII	IX	X
A	46	69	67	10	9	48	23	83	44	81
B	55	6	51	25	41	51	37	25	61	37
C	70	46	79	11	66	37	11	27	41	62
D	78	37	10	30	37	11	72	59	49	19
E	28	77	30	13	15	7	21	85	37	59
F	15	79	4	9	76	76	41	70	30	55
G	53	82	6	15	25	4	59	13	23	15
H	30	32	32	19	59	55	43	4	25	35
I	59	62	76	58	23	44	62	50	4	3
J	69	11	11	32	4	13	79	41	43	51
K	65	48	41	37	62	9	51	62	2	11
L	51	51	81	51	83	27	82	30	13	61
M	62	15	13	31	65	79	29	11	69	32
N	43	30	47	83	50	2	65	23	47	65
O	19	2	77	33	61	59	8	15	11	69
P	13	19	82	2	58	32	69	76	15	29
Q	76	75	21	4	79	21	32	55	82	76
R	48	4	37	46	2	62	46	79	32	2
S	6	81	65	12	43	23	26	82	6	45
T	41	57	59	48	10	15	13	65	59	79
U	5	36	19	78	82	25	2	21	76	21
V	11	21	15	59	51	19	48	2	19	82
W	79	13	2	41	11	26	4	69	46	63
X	32	25	25	62	30	30	25	19	21	48
Y	37	76	43	79	69	82	42	32	48	4
Z	82	41	46	53	19	41	55	37	51	13

| | I | II | III | IV | V | VI | VII | VIII | IX | X |

POSITION CHART

1	2	3	4	5
5	0	3	0	2
6	**7**	**8**	**9**	**10**
1	4, 8	2, 3	3	4
11	**12**	**13**	**14**	**15**
0	8	0	2	0
16	**17**	**18**	**19**	**20**
2	1	6	0	1, 3, 8
21	**22**	**23**	**24**	**25**
0	8	7	6	0
26	**27**	**28**	**29**	**30**
5	1	5, 6	4	0
31	**32**	**33**	**34**	**35**
5	0	6	8	2, 8
36	**37**	**38**	**39**	**40**
4	0	5	4, 7	4, 6, 7
41	**42**	**43**	**44**	**45**
0	8	0	2, 6	7
46	**47**	**48**	**49**	**50**
0	3	0	4	6
51	**52**	**53**	**54**	**55**
0	4	0	5	0
56	**57**	**58**	**59**	**60**
2	7	1	0	2
61	**62**	**63**	**64**	**65**
5	0	1	3	0
66	**67**	**68**	**69**	**70**
8	7	3	0	3, 4
71	**72**	**73**	**74**	**75**
1	1, 6	7	4	3
76	**77**	**78**	**79**	**80**
0	2, 5	7	0	6, 8
81	**82**	**83**	**84**	**85**
6	0	2	6	5, 8

LETTERS MISSED

I. ___ ___ ___ ___ ___ ___ ___
    1   2   3   4   5   6   7

II. ___ ___ ___ ___ ___ ___ ___
    1   2   3   4   5   6   7

III. ___ ___ ___ ___ ___ ___ ___
     1   2   3   4   5   6   7

IV. ___ ___ ___ ___ ___ ___ ___ ___
    1   2   3   4   5   6   7   8

V. ___ ___ ___ ___ ___ ___ ___ ___
    1   2   3   4   5   6   7   8

VI. ___ ___ ___ ___ ___ ___ ___ ___
    1   2   3   4   5   6   7   8

VII. ___ ___ ___ ___ ___ ___ ___ ___
     1   2   3   4   5   6   7   8

VIII. ___ ___ ___ ___ ___ ___ ___ ___
      1   2   3   4   5   6   7   8

IX. ___ ___ ___ ___ ___ ___ ___
    1   2   3   4   5   6   7

X. ___ ___ ___ ___ ___ ___ ___ ___
    1   2   3   4   5   6   7   8

Par Score: 7

Your Score: ___

SOLITAIRE HANGMAN

LETTER CHART

	I	II	III	IV	V	VI	VII	VIII	IX	X
A	30	34	41	21	40	47	39	43	92	65
B	69	56	69	11	25	23	83	90	69	48
C	80	17	48	24	74	49	77	2	84	61
D	36	87	27	95	27	18	17	8	79	52
E	22	78	45	53	17	41	48	31	87	11
F	71	48	32	84	56	65	52	48	56	2
G	32	65	71	27	32	27	66	11	71	69
H	48	52	8	73	2	48	51	92	28	1
I	2	69	79	71	52	77	73	56	22	6
J	17	32	11	48	69	56	56	65	8	71
K	52	71	42	36	48	8	69	57	2	13
L	58	18	56	58	7	2	46	52	27	79
M	8	75	80	8	90	32	32	69	65	83
N	56	81	85	45	26	36	79	77	50	29
O	3	77	59	52	65	52	27	13	5	50
P	38	82	77	17	18	69	36	71	32	80
Q	65	79	52	69	71	13	71	95	13	87
R	26	64	68	65	77	20	90	55	77	8
S	77	80	65	78	55	83	22	18	83	90
T	34	90	83	56	79	34	72	85	95	17
U	83	60	13	77	83	71	65	1	90	32
V	90	2	87	32	87	79	2	79	17	77
W	13	36	18	90	13	87	8	32	45	18
X	18	83	36	87	36	90	11	36	18	27
Y	27	8	2	79	8	11	87	83	11	56
Z	79	11	90	83	13	17	13	87	36	36
	I	II	III	IV	V	VI	VII	VIII	IX	X

POSITION CHART

1	2	3	4	5
7	0	4	1, 4, 9	7

6	7	8	9	10
2, 8	6	0	4	6

11	12	13	14	15
0	3, 10	0	1	10

16	17	18	19	20
8	0	0	4	5

21	22	23	24	25
3, 7	3	3	9	5

26	27	28	29	30
8	0	2	3	6, 9

31	32	33	34	35
1, 10	0	2	7	3

36	37	38	39	40
0	5, 8, 9	5	2	2, 4, 7, 10

41	42	43	44	45
6	7	2, 8	6	8

46	47	48	49	50
4	2, 4	0	1	49

51	52	53	54	55
7	0	10	7	3

56	57	58	59	60
0	9	2	2, 3	2

61	62	63	64	65
5, 6	10	9	5	0

66	67	68	69	70
1, 6	9	5, 9	0	3, 6

71	72	73	74	75
0	8	5	1, 9	6

76	77	78	79	80
2	0	4	0	1

81	82	83	84	85
8	3	0	1	4

86	87	88	89	90
1	0	8	1	0

91	92	93	94	95
10	5	4, 9	9	6

LETTERS MISSED

I. $\overline{}$
  1 2 3 4 5 6 7 8 9

II. $\overline{}$
  1 2 3 4 5 6 7 8

III. $\overline{}$
  1 2 3 4 5 6 7 8 9

IV. $\overline{}$
  1 2 3 4 5 6 7 8 9 10

V. $\overline{}$
  1 2 3 4 5 6 7 8 9 10

VI. $\overline{}$
  1 2 3 4 5 6 7

VII. $\overline{}$
  1 2 3 4 5 6 7 8

VIII. $\overline{}$
  1 2 3 4 5 6 7 8 9 10

IX. $\overline{}$
  1 2 3 4 5 6 7 8 9

X. $\overline{}$
  1 2 3 4 5 6 7 8 9

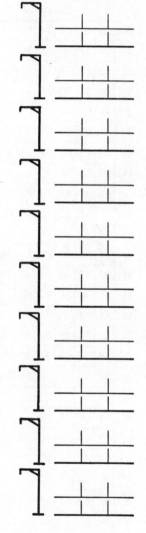

Par Score: 8

Your Score: ____

119

SOLITAIRE HANGMAN

LETTER CHART

	I	II	III	IV	V	VI	VII	VIII	IX	X
A	73	65	43	14	57	9	81	27	43	72
B	20	57	5	68	34	43	29	83	22	63
C	12	15	73	77	5	31	39	45	45	5
D	26	83	80	15	41	72	48	75	67	26
E	24	73	74	63	53	62	80	25	62	2
F	5	29	26	45	8	78	64	62	46	29
G	53	20	78	34	56	60	26	46	29	68
H	80	78	52	48	45	73	57	58	34	73
I	40	5	83	75	36	36	78	5	6	15
J	78	31	45	47	46	80	43	50	78	8
K	15	45	48	5	10	83	5	8	80	34
L	34	69	65	78	50	26	77	24	60	78
M	29	49	46	24	43	15	34	10	31	36
N	2	4	56	83	58	19	53	15	17	9
O	31	84	7	8	6	57	72	20	53	66
P	43	68	63	29	51	20	45	26	26	20
Q	56	34	68	64	60	29	50	48	64	43
R	36	37	8	20	75	24	40	6	5	31
S	45	46	10	19	85	68	15	43	54	24
T	81	56	58	49	48	47	46	29	84	58
U	58	26	20	60	15	32	56	53	14	45
V	60	8	50	26	68	45	20	56	56	48
W	8	10	15	10	52	58	31	32	48	83
X	57	80	34	31	20	56	8	73	68	46
Y	10	64	60	73	62	34	68	78	50	18
Z	46	36	29	36	31	8	58	31	73	80

	I	II	III	IV	V	VI	VII	VIII	IX	X

POSITION CHART

1	2	3	4	5
3	5	2, 7	3	0

6	7	8	9	10
6	2, 3, 6	0	7	0

11	12	13	14	15
3	6	4	2	0

16	17	18	19	20
2	7	3	5	0

21	22	23	24	25
7	5	6	1	2, 3

26	27	28	29	30
0	5	6	0	7

31	32	33	34	35
0	4	7	0	6, 8

36	37	38	39	40
0	5	2, 8	1, 5	4

41	42	43	44	45
8	8	0	1, 5	0

46	47	48	49	50
0	3	0	6	0

51	52	53	54	55
1	5	0	3	1

56	57	58	59	60
0	2	0	2	0

61	62	63	64	65
1	0	4	0	1, 7

66	67	68	69	70
2	1	0	8	5, 6

71	72	73	74	75
4	6	0	8	7

76	77	78	79	80
1	8	0	2, 5, 6	0

81	82	83	84	85
3, 7	2	0	4	3, 4

POTPOURRI 8

LETTERS MISSED

I. $\overline{\underset{1}{\quad}\,\underset{2}{\quad}\,\underset{3}{\quad}\,\underset{4}{\quad}\,\underset{5}{\quad}\,\underset{6}{\quad}\,\underset{7}{\quad}}$

II. $\overline{\underset{1}{\quad}\,\underset{2}{\quad}\,\underset{3}{\quad}\,\underset{4}{\quad}\,\underset{5}{\quad}\,\underset{6}{\quad}\,\underset{7}{\quad}\,\underset{8}{\quad}}$

III. $\overline{\underset{1}{\quad}\,\underset{2}{\quad}\,\underset{3}{\quad}\,\underset{4}{\quad}\,\underset{5}{\quad}\,\underset{6}{\quad}\,\underset{7}{\quad}\,\underset{8}{\quad}}$

IV. $\overline{\underset{1}{\quad}\,\underset{2}{\quad}\,\underset{3}{\quad}\,\underset{4}{\quad}\,\underset{5}{\quad}\,\underset{6}{\quad}\,\underset{7}{\quad}\,\underset{8}{\quad}}$

V. $\overline{\underset{1}{\quad}\,\underset{2}{\quad}\,\underset{3}{\quad}\,\underset{4}{\quad}\,\underset{5}{\quad}\,\underset{6}{\quad}\,\underset{7}{\quad}\,\underset{8}{\quad}}$

VI. $\overline{\underset{1}{\quad}\,\underset{2}{\quad}\,\underset{3}{\quad}\,\underset{4}{\quad}\,\underset{5}{\quad}\,\underset{6}{\quad}\,\underset{7}{\quad}}$

VII. $\overline{\underset{1}{\quad}\,\underset{2}{\quad}\,\underset{3}{\quad}\,\underset{4}{\quad}\,\underset{5}{\quad}\,\underset{6}{\quad}\,\underset{7}{\quad}\,\underset{8}{\quad}}$

VIII. $\overline{\underset{1}{\quad}\,\underset{2}{\quad}\,\underset{3}{\quad}\,\underset{4}{\quad}\,\underset{5}{\quad}\,\underset{6}{\quad}\,\underset{7}{\quad}}$

IX. $\overline{\underset{1}{\quad}\,\underset{2}{\quad}\,\underset{3}{\quad}\,\underset{4}{\quad}\,\underset{5}{\quad}\,\underset{6}{\quad}\,\underset{7}{\quad}}$

X. $\overline{\underset{1}{\quad}\,\underset{2}{\quad}\,\underset{3}{\quad}\,\underset{4}{\quad}\,\underset{5}{\quad}\,\underset{6}{\quad}\,\underset{7}{\quad}}$

Par Score: 7

Your Score: _____

SOLITAIRE HANGMAN

LETTER CHART

	I	II	III	IV	V	VI	VII	VIII	IX	X
A	9	36	31	34	44	32	50	73	54	10
B	51	21	8	3	28	18	73	75	53	43
C	41	47	3	62	62	83	3	29	34	47
D	73	31	69	26	30	3	23	3	51	51
E	47	74	72	63	26	23	56	74	15	3
F	75	66	47	29	6	34	18	6	29	54
G	35	11	15	64	68	26	12	53	3	60
H	26	56	44	15	12	21	43	8	39	77
I	19	75	62	18	74	78	26	43	74	6
J	34	43	26	6	3	73	62	11	6	26
K	6	51	43	31	15	51	6	15	18	29
L	43	55	56	48	29	4	15	52	77	66
M	11	83	6	37	21	27	11	18	56	52
N	45	26	64	68	8	29	37	64	62	33
O	12	12	12	23	73	43	1	26	70	12
P	37	29	65	35	18	64	66	31	31	62
Q	3	34	18	39	31	31	29	54	66	15
R	39	42	67	20	83	66	67	30	26	56
S	8	62	11	43	34	45	39	34	30	64
T	29	54	29	47	37	5	83	68	45	31
U	15	37	73	12	43	6	68	14	37	68
V	31	3	34	51	66	37	75	37	8	34
W	54	39	37	54	39	68	34	39	64	8
X	56	64	39	61	47	39	64	12	43	18
Y	62	73	51	56	51	47	31	47	23	37
Z	64	6	54	66	54	54	47	51	68	73
	I	II	III	IV	V	VI	VII	VIII	IX	X

POSITION CHART

1	2	3	4	5
6	8	0	2	9
6	**7**	**8**	**9**	**10**
0	4	0	2, 7	2, 6
11	**12**	**13**	**14**	**15**
1	0	8	2	0
16	**17**	**18**	**19**	**20**
2, 6, 7	2	0	4, 6	6, 8
21	**22**	**23**	**24**	**25**
4	1, 7	5	5	3
26	**27**	**28**	**29**	**30**
0	6	1	0	7
31	**32**	**33**	**34**	**35**
0	1	3, 7	0	3
36	**37**	**38**	**39**	**40**
2	0	6	0	6
41	**42**	**43**	**44**	**45**
5	7	0	2, 5	8
46	**47**	**48**	**49**	**50**
3	0	4	7	2, 4
51	**52**	**53**	**54**	**55**
0	5	3, 4	0	5
56	**57**	**58**	**59**	**60**
0	3	5	3	4
61	**62**	**63**	**64**	**65**
2	0	1, 7	0	4
66	**67**	**68**	**69**	**70**
0	7	0	8	2
71	**72**	**73**	**74**	**75**
7	3, 6	0	6	0
76	**77**	**78**	**79**	**80**
6	1	7	8	1
81	**82**	**83**	**84**	**85**
4	1	3	2, 9	8

LETTERS MISSED

I. — — — — — — — —
  1 2 3 4 5 6 7 8

II. — — — — — — —
  1 2 3 4 5 6 7

III. — — — — — — — —
  1 2 3 4 5 6 7 8

IV. — — — — — — — —
  1 2 3 4 5 6 7 8

V. — — — — — — —
  1 2 3 4 5 6 7

VI. — — — — — — — — —
  1 2 3 4 5 6 7 8 9

VII. — — — — — — —
  1 2 3 4 5 6 7

VIII. — — — — — — —
  1 2 3 4 5 6 7

IX. — — — — — — — —
  1 2 3 4 5 6 7 8

X. — — — — — — —
  1 2 3 4 5 6 7

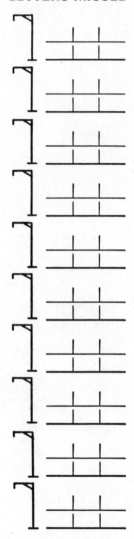

Par Score: 7

Your Score: ____

SOLITAIRE HANGMAN

LETTER CHART

	I	II	III	IV	V	VI	VII	VIII	IX	X
A	7	40	11	78	26	42	19	4	43	29
B	43	18	4	26	74	23	74	65	72	20
C	23	37	66	80	36	15	23	27	23	47
D	74	21	51	5	22	74	43	7	64	83
E	79	31	39	47	14	18	35	45	35	31
F	12	74	47	15	82	52	78	62	78	43
G	78	26	52	52	29	78	64	78	62	52
H	42	27	7	37	52	58	80	81	80	66
I	60	32	61	23	80	43	21	52	60	64
J	9	15	43	54	25	33	70	47	47	25
K	62	58	9	66	62	69	4	80	13	80
L	52	19	68	58	78	64	11	25	37	6
M	47	23	54	27	33	7	46	82	4	35
N	4	47	72	21	64	29	7	54	21	9
O	70	25	58	38	9	49	59	43	83	27
P	11	29	65	62	21	85	9	9	82	33
Q	54	52	74	64	19	54	58	64	68	21
R	37	5	10	25	43	73	34	14	18	70
S	83	43	82	33	54	62	56	11	65	4
T	15	4	17	18	16	10	39	26	58	23
U	29	82	62	68	55	4	25	74	66	72
V	58	33	27	29	47	80	15	18	25	68
W	18	78	21	70	58	47	27	58	70	74
X	21	54	64	74	4	68	62	66	7	18
Y	25	80	15	35	66	70	18	69	52	54
Z	82	7	70	43	18	82	68	23	74	78
	I	II	III	IV	V	VI	VII	VIII	IX	X

POSITION CHART

1	2	3	4	5
1, 4	1	2	0	7
6	**7**	**8**	**9**	**10**
7, 8	0	3, 7	0	4
11	**12**	**13**	**14**	**15**
0	6, 7	7	4	0
16	**17**	**18**	**19**	**20**
8	3	0	2	4, 5
21	**22**	**23**	**24**	**25**
0	5	0	5	0
26	**27**	**28**	**29**	**30**
1	0	8	0	1, 7, 8
31	**32**	**33**	**34**	**35**
6	5	0	6	3
36	**37**	**38**	**39**	**40**
7	4	2, 5, 6	5	3
41	**42**	**43**	**44**	**45**
6	2	0	4	3, 5
46	**47**	**48**	**49**	**50**
1	0	3	5, 6	1
51	**52**	**53**	**54**	**55**
8	0	8	0	3, 6
56	**57**	**58**	**59**	**60**
4	4	0	7	5
61	**62**	**63**	**64**	**65**
1, 7	0	5	0	6
66	**67**	**68**	**69**	**70**
0	8	0	7	0
71	**72**	**73**	**74**	**75**
6	2	3	0	1, 3
76	**77**	**78**	**79**	**80**
3	2	0	3	0
81	**82**	**83**	**84**	**85**
2	0	1	6	1

I. $\overline{1}$ $\overline{2}$ $\overline{3}$ $\overline{4}$ $\overline{5}$ $\overline{6}$ $\overline{7}$

II. $\overline{1}$ $\overline{2}$ $\overline{3}$ $\overline{4}$ $\overline{5}$ $\overline{6}$ $\overline{7}$

III. $\overline{1}$ $\overline{2}$ $\overline{3}$ $\overline{4}$ $\overline{5}$ $\overline{6}$ $\overline{7}$ $\overline{8}$

IV. $\overline{1}$ $\overline{2}$ $\overline{3}$ $\overline{4}$ $\overline{5}$ $\overline{6}$ $\overline{7}$

V. $\overline{1}$ $\overline{2}$ $\overline{3}$ $\overline{4}$ $\overline{5}$ $\overline{6}$ $\overline{7}$ $\overline{8}$

VI. $\overline{1}$ $\overline{2}$ $\overline{3}$ $\overline{4}$ $\overline{5}$ $\overline{6}$ $\overline{7}$

VII. $\overline{1}$ $\overline{2}$ $\overline{3}$ $\overline{4}$ $\overline{5}$ $\overline{6}$ $\overline{7}$

VIII. $\overline{1}$ $\overline{2}$ $\overline{3}$ $\overline{4}$ $\overline{5}$ $\overline{6}$ $\overline{7}$

IX. $\overline{1}$ $\overline{2}$ $\overline{3}$ $\overline{4}$ $\overline{5}$ $\overline{6}$ $\overline{7}$

X. $\overline{1}$ $\overline{2}$ $\overline{3}$ $\overline{4}$ $\overline{5}$ $\overline{6}$ $\overline{7}$ $\overline{8}$

Par Score: 6

Your Score: _____

SOLITAIRE HANGMAN

LETTER CHART

	I	II	III	IV	V	VI	VII	VIII	IX	X
A	83	54	58	46	75	55	30	58	9	11
B	76	49	20	5	46	83	17	22	63	65
C	7	63	68	60	83	5	41	41	12	10
D	20	5	83	41	57	7	84	79	57	46
E	74	83	50	7	34	56	52	2	61	40
F	36	28	49	11	65	20	69	13	56	83
G	41	20	51	63	69	11	5	83	60	57
H	59	65	13	36	5	41	46	5	65	5
I	21	11	69	47	13	17	9	57	45	27
J	5	61	5	69	18	49	28	17	36	22
K	46	40	79	43	7	22	83	30	69	17
L	69	15	60	32	19	14	51	60	83	71
M	43	41	30	19	41	46	32	7	11	13
N	11	7	57	82	11	28	57	28	5	18
O	60	13	21	53	20	21	36	69	49	43
P	49	69	61	51	36	30	58	11	13	28
Q	63	46	22	49	43	32	60	63	41	20
R	51	17	28	30	22	65	7	32	17	49
S	13	18	32	62	28	13	63	61	32	30
T	28	22	17	13	71	37	79	65	20	67
U	57	30	63	57	30	43	11	36	43	48
V	71	32	7	17	45	18	65	18	22	36
W	17	3	18	65	60	51	49	78	28	63
X	65	36	65	18	32	63	19	20	30	41
Y	18	67	11	20	17	57	43	43	26	7
Z	32	43	43	83	49	36	13	46	18	51

I II III IV V VI VII VIII IX X

POSITION CHART

1	2	3	4	5
4	2,5,6	4	7	0
6	**7**	**8**	**9**	**10**
7	0	5	6	1,5
11	**12**	**13**	**14**	**15**
0	5,7	0	8	6
16	**17**	**18**	**19**	**20**
1	0	0	2	0
21	**22**	**23**	**24**	**25**
5	0	3	1,4	6
26	**27**	**28**	**29**	**30**
8	4	0	8	0
31	**32**	**33**	**34**	**35**
2	0	8	1,3,7	1
36	**37**	**38**	**39**	**40**
0	1,4,6	1	5,8	7
41	**42**	**43**	**44**	**45**
0	2	0	5	4
46	**47**	**48**	**49**	**50**
0	3,6	2	0	2
51	**52**	**53**	**54**	**55**
0	1,4,8	1,7	2,5	7
56	**57**	**58**	**59**	**60**
2,3	0	3	4	0
61	**62**	**63**	**64**	**65**
1	4,5	0	3	0
66	**67**	**68**	**69**	**70**
7	3	4,6	0	3
71	**72**	**73**	**74**	**75**
6	3	2	2,3,7	5
76	**77**	**78**	**79**	**80**
1	5	4	7	1
81	**82**	**83**	**84**	**85**
6	8	0	5	5,8

TAKE A LETTER

LETTERS MISSED

I. $\overline{\quad 1 \quad 2 \quad 3 \quad 4 \quad 5 \quad 6 \quad 7 \quad}$

II. $\overline{\quad 1 \quad 2 \quad 3 \quad 4 \quad 5 \quad 6 \quad 7 \quad}$

III. $\overline{\quad 1 \quad 2 \quad 3 \quad 4 \quad 5 \quad 6 \quad 7 \quad}$

IV. $\overline{\quad 1 \quad 2 \quad 3 \quad 4 \quad 5 \quad 6 \quad 7 \quad 8 \quad}$

V. $\overline{\quad 1 \quad 2 \quad 3 \quad 4 \quad 5 \quad 6 \quad 7 \quad}$

VI. $\overline{\quad 1 \quad 2 \quad 3 \quad 4 \quad 5 \quad 6 \quad 7 \quad 8 \quad}$

VII. $\overline{\quad 1 \quad 2 \quad 3 \quad 4 \quad 5 \quad 6 \quad 7 \quad 8 \quad}$

VIII. $\overline{\quad 1 \quad 2 \quad 3 \quad 4 \quad 5 \quad 6 \quad 7 \quad}$

IX. $\overline{\quad 1 \quad 2 \quad 3 \quad 4 \quad 5 \quad 6 \quad 7 \quad 8 \quad}$

X. $\overline{\quad 1 \quad 2 \quad 3 \quad 4 \quad 5 \quad 6 \quad 7 \quad}$

Par Score: 7

Your Score: ___

SOLITAIRE HANGMAN

LETTER CHART

	I	II	III	IV	V	VI	VII	VIII	IX	X
A	45	68	74	11	44	29	5	69	82	82
B	81	2	51	25	56	49	37	25	6	37
C	30	48	79	8	49	42	8	30	39	32
D	43	39	82	30	37	11	13	61	66	19
E	76	77	84	33	15	83	21	19	36	72
F	15	65	5	5	76	76	39	2	30	55
G	55	82	73	15	25	5	55	46	45	46
H	29	32	30	31	61	55	28	10	25	5
I	77	61	76	47	5	52	60	47	18	83
J	67	5	8	32	8	15	79	39	37	51
K	63	47	41	37	63	32	49	63	85	11
L	51	50	55	51	73	7	78	32	17	76
M	61	15	11	16	6	71	30	8	69	63
N	79	30	15	69	39	19	65	23	43	74
O	46	67	61	46	65	61	33	1	12	65
P	17	19	85	19	67	79	63	76	8	21
Q	82	85	21	21	79	21	32	55	5	67
R	56	83	46	4	85	63	41	81	23	49
S	85	79	71	58	36	25	19	79	76	39
T	42	66	1	48	11	46	9	65	61	35
U	5	37	19	39	82	30	82	21	79	15
V	8	21	25	61	51	8	43	82	3	2
W	69	8	32	41	19	37	2	67	41	69
X	32	25	37	63	30	85	25	15	32	61
Y	37	11	80	79	75	39	45	37	49	85
Z	65	76	39	55	21	41	61	85	21	8
	I	II	III	IV	V	VI	VII	VIII	IX	X

POSITION CHART

1	2	3	4	5
2, 5	1	3	7	0
6	**7**	**8**	**9**	**10**
5	5, 6	0	3	4
11	**12**	**13**	**14**	**15**
0	2	8	2	0
16	**17**	**18**	**19**	**20**
2	1	6	0	4, 8
21	**22**	**23**	**24**	**25**
0	8	7	6	0
26	**27**	**28**	**29**	**30**
5	1	4, 5	4	0
31	**32**	**33**	**34**	**35**
5	0	6	8	6, 7
36	**37**	**38**	**39**	**40**
4	0	5	0	3, 8
41	**42**	**43**	**44**	**45**
0	8	0	1, 6	0
46	**47**	**48**	**49**	**50**
3	0	4	0	6
51	**52**	**53**	**54**	**55**
0	7	4	5	0
56	**57**	**58**	**59**	**60**
2	7	1	5	2
61	**62**	**63**	**64**	**65**
0	1	0	3	0
66	**67**	**68**	**69**	**70**
8	0	3	0	1, 7
71	**72**	**73**	**74**	**75**
1	5, 8	7	4	3
76	**77**	**78**	**79**	**80**
0	5, 7	7	0	8
81	**82**	**83**	**84**	**85**
6	0	2	6	0

LETTERS MISSED

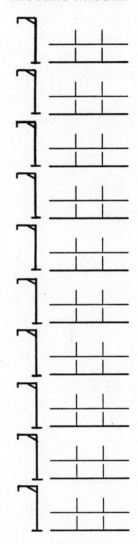

I. $\overline{}_{1}\ \overline{}_{2}\ \overline{}_{3}\ \overline{}_{4}\ \overline{}_{5}\ \overline{}_{6}\ \overline{}_{7}\ \overline{}_{8}$

II. $\overline{}_{1}\ \overline{}_{2}\ \overline{}_{3}\ \overline{}_{4}\ \overline{}_{5}\ \overline{}_{6}\ \overline{}_{7}\ \overline{}_{8}$

III. $\overline{}_{1}\ \overline{}_{2}\ \overline{}_{3}\ \overline{}_{4}\ \overline{}_{5}\ \overline{}_{6}\ \overline{}_{7}\ \overline{}_{8}$

IV. $\overline{}_{1}\ \overline{}_{2}\ \overline{}_{3}\ \overline{}_{4}\ \overline{}_{5}\ \overline{}_{6}\ \overline{}_{7}$

V. $\overline{}_{1}\ \overline{}_{2}\ \overline{}_{3}\ \overline{}_{4}\ \overline{}_{5}\ \overline{}_{6}\ \overline{}_{7}$

VI. $\overline{}_{1}\ \overline{}_{2}\ \overline{}_{3}\ \overline{}_{4}\ \overline{}_{5}\ \overline{}_{6}\ \overline{}_{7}\ \overline{}_{8}$

VII. $\overline{}_{1}\ \overline{}_{2}\ \overline{}_{3}\ \overline{}_{4}\ \overline{}_{5}\ \overline{}_{6}\ \overline{}_{7}\ \overline{}_{8}$

VIII. $\overline{}_{1}\ \overline{}_{2}\ \overline{}_{3}\ \overline{}_{4}\ \overline{}_{5}\ \overline{}_{6}\ \overline{}_{7}$

IX. $\overline{}_{1}\ \overline{}_{2}\ \overline{}_{3}\ \overline{}_{4}\ \overline{}_{5}\ \overline{}_{6}\ \overline{}_{7}\ \overline{}_{8}$

X. $\overline{}_{1}\ \overline{}_{2}\ \overline{}_{3}\ \overline{}_{4}\ \overline{}_{5}\ \overline{}_{6}\ \overline{}_{7}\ \overline{}_{8}$

Par Score: 6   Your Score: ____

SOLITAIRE HANGMAN

LETTER CHART

	I	II	III	IV	V	VI	VII	VIII	IX	X
A	77	72	61	57	71	8	5	29	87	79
B	45	57	30	48	5	65	37	90	79	22
C	17	87	40	22	66	79	65	25	37	87
D	88	74	64	14	78	90	1	65	69	13
E	93	61	43	19	87	53	73	81	65	3
F	33	30	79	73	14	43	90	73	14	73
G	83	90	52	75	36	73	43	27	33	54
H	94	79	22	79	79	22	4	79	67	14
I	47	65	94	68	90	52	88	83	22	26
J	30	69	25	65	43	45	75	78	52	43
K	14	94	38	83	54	25	79	54	54	56
L	44	75	80	89	4	36	30	94	43	83
M	36	37	33	5	94	75	83	87	25	45
N	76	19	58	8	56	42	16	39	48	76
O	22	8	29	86	65	54	85	36	50	59
P	54	73	36	25	22	7	87	43	30	90
Q	90	22	54	27	75	27	54	30	94	61
R	4	83	45	87	95	62	69	34	60	48
S	27	2	90	61	45	48	94	5	27	94
T	73	25	73	33	83	6	14	14	88	1
U	25	33	42	30	9	14	22	22	45	80
V	43	43	87	36	25	83	52	75	83	25
W	65	54	5	90	27	94	25	33	8	30
X	48	56	48	43	30	56	33	52	90	10
Y	56	45	14	45	48	87	27	4	5	27
Z	52	14	27	94	52	30	36	48	75	33

	I	II	III	IV	V	VI	VII	VIII	IX	X

POSITION CHART

1	2	3	4	5
9	5	10	6	0
6	**7**	**8**	**9**	**10**
3	1, 6	7	5	7
11	**12**	**13**	**14**	**15**
7	2	1	0	10
16	**17**	**18**	**19**	**20**
5	1	4	8	5
21	**22**	**23**	**24**	**25**
7	0	4	8	0
26	**27**	**28**	**29**	**30**
6	0	6	2	0
31	**32**	**33**	**34**	**35**
10	1, 10	0	7	4, 9
36	**37**	**38**	**39**	**40**
0	3	10	3	9
41	**42**	**43**	**44**	**45**
9	8	0	8, 9	0
46	**47**	**48**	**49**	**50**
7	2	0	3, 7, 9	2, 5, 9
51	**52**	**53**	**54**	**55**
9	0	2, 4	0	4, 10
56	**57**	**58**	**59**	**60**
0	6	3	2, 8	6
61	**62**	**63**	**64**	**65**
4	5	6	1, 6, 7	0
66	**67**	**68**	**69**	**70**
4	8	3	1	8
71	**72**	**73**	**74**	**75**
3, 7	2	0	9	0
76	**77**	**78**	**79**	**80**
3	10	1	0	5
81	**82**	**83**	**84**	**85**
4, 5, 8	8	0	1	2, 7, 8
86	**87**	**88**	**89**	**90**
2	0	4	1, 5	0
91	**92**	**93**	**94**	**95**
4	1	5, 7	0	2

LETTERS MISSED

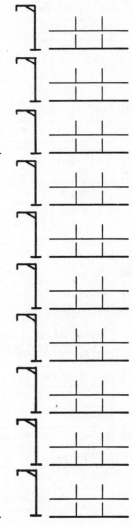

I. $\overline{}_{1} \ \overline{}_{2} \ \overline{}_{3} \ \overline{}_{4} \ \overline{}_{5} \ \overline{}_{6} \ \overline{}_{7} \ \overline{}_{8} \ \overline{}_{9} \ \overline{}_{10}$

II. $\overline{}_{1} \ \overline{}_{2} \ \overline{}_{3} \ \overline{}_{4} \ \overline{}_{5} \ \overline{}_{6} \ \overline{}_{7} \ \overline{}_{8} \ \overline{}_{9}$

III. $\overline{}_{1} \ \overline{}_{2} \ \overline{}_{3} \ \overline{}_{4} \ \overline{}_{5} \ \overline{}_{6} \ \overline{}_{7} \ \overline{}_{8} \ \overline{}_{9} \ \overline{}_{10}$

IV. $\overline{}_{1} \ \overline{}_{2} \ \overline{}_{3} \ \overline{}_{4} \ \overline{}_{5} \ \overline{}_{6} \ \overline{}_{7} \ \overline{}_{8}$

V. $\overline{}_{1} \ \overline{}_{2} \ \overline{}_{3} \ \overline{}_{4} \ \overline{}_{5} \ \overline{}_{6} \ \overline{}_{7}$

VI. $\overline{}_{1} \ \overline{}_{2} \ \overline{}_{3} \ \overline{}_{4} \ \overline{}_{5} \ \overline{}_{6} \ \overline{}_{7} \ \overline{}_{8}$

VII. $\overline{}_{1} \ \overline{}_{2} \ \overline{}_{3} \ \overline{}_{4} \ \overline{}_{5} \ \overline{}_{6} \ \overline{}_{7} \ \overline{}_{8} \ \overline{}_{9}$

VIII. $\overline{}_{1} \ \overline{}_{2} \ \overline{}_{3} \ \overline{}_{4} \ \overline{}_{5} \ \overline{}_{6} \ \overline{}_{7} \ \overline{}_{8}$

IX. $\overline{}_{1} \ \overline{}_{2} \ \overline{}_{3} \ \overline{}_{4} \ \overline{}_{5} \ \overline{}_{6} \ \overline{}_{7} \ \overline{}_{8} \ \overline{}_{9}$

X. $\overline{}_{1} \ \overline{}_{2} \ \overline{}_{3} \ \overline{}_{4} \ \overline{}_{5} \ \overline{}_{6} \ \overline{}_{7} \ \overline{}_{8} \ \overline{}_{9} \ \overline{}_{10}$

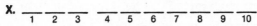

Par Score: 8

Your Score: _____

SOLITAIRE HANGMAN

LETTER CHART

	I	II	III	IV	V	VI	VII	VIII	IX	X
A	73	64	39	5	47	44	83	41	3	73
B	20	51	81	68	72	39	27	4	20	58
C	75	15	73	78	5	43	63	45	52	5
D	32	1	80	15	1	63	69	63	69	41
E	41	4	3	85	54	46	84	83	63	65
F	9	34	26	45	8	75	65	65	45	25
G	54	20	75	34	39	60	26	46	27	46
H	80	17	48	48	43	1	54	58	34	75
I	85	5	4	1	58	8	57	5	24	15
J	78	36	43	46	36	78	43	50	75	8
K	15	45	50	8	45	41	5	8	80	34
L	7	48	72	80	50	26	78	10	72	3
M	26	39	45	3	46	18	34	75	36	36
N	68	26	56	10	64	10	55	9	64	45
O	27	73	78	20	80	57	68	19	55	85
P	39	68	46	26	48	20	36	32	26	20
Q	56	27	76	4	56	15	48	48	65	39
R	34	57	58	24	34	27	33	78	14	32
S	43	46	8	27	53	68	15	51	54	26
T	58	72	54	36	14	51	39	20	5	60
U	60	43	57	64	10	45	56	57	8	47
V	63	8	5	39	68	36	24	56	56	78
W	24	10	10	43	15	3	45	34	48	27
X	36	75	34	50	20	54	8	73	68	43
Y	8	63	60	73	3	34	1	15	50	68
Z	45	50	15	54	60	65	46	26	73	10
	I	II	III	IV	V	VI	VII	VIII	IX	X

POSITION CHART

1 / 5	**2** / 3, 4, 8	**3** / 7	**4** / 3	**5** / 0
6 / 6	**7** / 3, 5	**8** / 0	**9** / 7	**10** / 0
11 / 3	**12** / 6	**13** / 4	**14** / 2	**15** / 0
16 / 2	**17** / 7	**18** / 3	**19** / 5	**20** / 0
21 / 7	**22** / 5	**23** / 6	**24** / 1	**25** / 1, 5
26 / 0	**27** / 0	**28** / 6	**29** / 5	**30** / 7
31 / 3	**32** / 4	**33** / 7	**34** / 0	**35** / 1, 3
36 / 0	**37** / 5	**38** / 5, 7	**39** / 0	**40** / 4
41 / 8	**42** / 8	**43** / 0	**44** / 4, 6	**45** / 0
46 / 0	**47** / 3	**48** / 0	**49** / 4, 7	**50** / 0
51 / 1	**52** / 5	**53** / 1	**54** / 0	**55** / 3
56 / 0	**57** / 2	**58** / 0	**59** / 2	**60** / 0
61 / 1	**62** / 1, 8	**63** / 0	**64** / 4	**65** / 0
66 / 2	**67** / 1	**68** / 0	**69** / 8	**70** / 2, 5, 6
71 / 4	**72** / 6	**73** / 0	**74** / 8	**75** / 0
76 / 1	**77** / 8	**78** / 0	**79** / 2, 3	**80** / 0
81 / 4, 5	**82** / 2	**83** / 6	**84** / 4	**85** / 2, 6

LETTERS MISSED

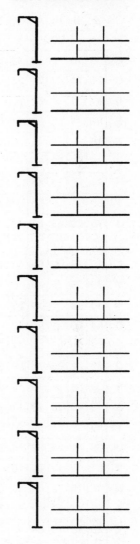

I. $\overline{\ \ \ \ \ \ \ \ \ \ \ \ \ \ \ \ \ }$
    1   2   3   4   5   6   7   8

II. $\overline{\ \ \ \ \ \ \ \ \ \ \ \ \ \ }$
    1   2   3   4   5   6   7

III. $\overline{\ \ \ \ \ \ \ \ \ \ \ \ \ \ }$
    1   2   3   4   5   6   7

IV. $\overline{\ \ \ \ \ \ \ \ \ \ \ \ \ \ }$
    1   2   3   4   5   6   7

V. $\overline{\ \ \ \ \ \ \ \ \ \ \ \ \ \ }$
    1   2   3   4   5   6   7

VI. $\overline{\ \ \ \ \ \ \ \ \ \ \ \ \ \ \ \ \ }$
    1   2   3   4   5   6   7   8

VII. $\overline{\ \ \ \ \ \ \ \ \ \ \ \ \ \ \ \ \ }$
    1   2   3   4   5   6   7   8

VIII. $\overline{\ \ \ \ \ \ \ \ \ \ \ \ \ \ \ \ \ }$
    1   2   3   4   5   6   7   8

IX. $\overline{\ \ \ \ \ \ \ \ \ \ \ \ \ \ \ \ \ }$
    1   2   3   4   5   6   7   8

X. $\overline{\ \ \ \ \ \ \ \ \ \ \ \ \ \ \ \ \ }$
    1   2   3   4   5   6   7   8

Par Score: 6

Your Score: _____

SOLITAIRE HANGMAN

LETTER CHART

	I	II	III	IV	V	VI	VII	VIII	IX	X
A	84	63	79	55	8	12	36	26	15	72
B	55	16	55	43	32	61	45	51	56	84
C	21	71	47	71	25	45	18	10	11	81
D	41	23	81	67	36	25	8	12	14	14
E	67	39	30	85	41	69	76	84	40	55
F	16	5	78	41	3	83	14	25	45	43
G	59	55	59	36	16	32	41	7	32	3
H	71	67	28	45	5	20	32	76	76	11
I	66	8	3	58	27	78	21	79	67	63
J	76	59	43	81	43	36	16	36	47	25
K	73	84	67	8	69	41	29	41	43	32
L	10	78	7	69	67	71	62	2	60	45
M	79	25	25	29	2	79	75	8	16	59
N	80	14	5	18	55	14	79	81	29	30
O	54	30	21	25	50	3	66	3	79	5
P	83	29	69	59	47	47	25	5	41	2
Q	32	32	36	76	29	55	55	32	59	76
R	29	36	32	12	59	48	60	69	46	35
S	19	43	48	73	12	38	2	14	5	79
T	69	19	71	49	60	21	81	55	36	10
U	36	41	23	32	74	59	67	78	61	36
V	81	10	41	79	18	73	43	16	81	8
W	3	45	73	61	10	67	83	43	18	16
X	43	61	84	47	61	76	47	67	84	41
Y	25	18	75	84	45	84	59	48	3	18
Z	5	47	61	3	71	43	61	18	55	47
	I	II	III	IV	V	VI	VII	VIII	IX	X

POSITION CHART

1	2	3	4	5
2,4,8	1	0	2	0
6	**7**	**8**	**9**	**10**
8	7	0	1,6,7	0
11	**12**	**13**	**14**	**15**
6	3	3,4,6	0	2,5
16	**17**	**18**	**19**	**20**
0	7,8	0	1	8
21	**22**	**23**	**24**	**25**
2	1	3	6	0
26	**27**	**28**	**29**	**30**
2	6	1	4	5
31	**32**	**33**	**34**	**35**
4	0	1	7	3
36	**37**	**38**	**39**	**40**
0	6	1,7	7	8
41	**42**	**43**	**44**	**45**
0	7	0	3,5	0
46	**47**	**48**	**49**	**50**
3	0	4	1,6	2,8
51	**52**	**53**	**54**	**55**
5	4	4	3,7	0
56	**57**	**58**	**59**	**60**
1	3	5	0	7
61	**62**	**63**	**64**	**65**
0	3	2	7	5
66	**67**	**68**	**69**	**70**
6	0	1,5	0	2
71	**72**	**73**	**74**	**75**
0	4,7	0	5	8
76	**77**	**78**	**79**	**80**
0	4	6	0	8
81	**82**	**83**	**84**	**85**
0	2	5	0	2,7

LITTLE CRITTERS

LETTERS MISSED

I. $\overline{}\ \overline{}\ \overline{}\ \overline{}\ \overline{}\ \overline{}\ \overline{}\ \overline{}$
  1 2 3 4 5 6 7 8

II. $\overline{}\ \overline{}\ \overline{}\ \overline{}\ \overline{}\ \overline{}\ \overline{}$
  1 2 3 4 5 6 7

III. 1 2 3 4 5 6 7 8

IV. 1 2 3 4 5 6 7

V. 1 2 3 4 5 6 7 8

VI. 1 2 3 4 5 6 7 8

VII. 1 2 3 4 5 6 7 8

VIII. 1 2 3 4 5 6 7

IX. 1 2 3 4 5 6 7 8

X. 1 2 3 4 5 6 7

Par Score: 7

Your Score: _____

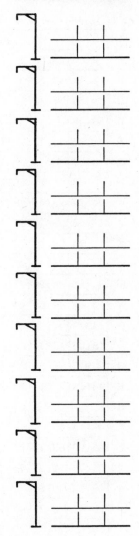

SOLITAIRE HANGMAN

LETTER CHART

	I	II	III	IV	V	VI	VII	VIII	IX	X
A	68	73	84	62	63	66	69	35	16	72
B	29	60	59	68	15	81	4	59	30	60
C	70	11	47	32	4	27	15	47	74	82
D	47	76	74	18	55	15	47	75	21	9
E	58	25	7	70	6	4	68	28	9	47
F	9	47	35	15	21	55	70	49	60	78
G	32	29	4	14	9	21	84	9	35	36
H	12	49	21	23	68	39	5	15	78	81
I	24	78	26	49	18	9	54	36	81	55
J	13	68	39	34	81	60	29	29	13	49
K	19	70	55	13	78	70	13	74	57	13
L	83	61	44	4	71	44	55	55	4	23
M	81	55	32	26	12	74	49	25	15	26
N	28	81	49	69	44	25	14	60	75	70
O	74	71	9	20	7	13	78	68	6	74
P	15	35	13	74	47	47	9	84	55	18
Q	4	13	76	39	32	76	76	21	68	25
R	18	39	23	67	22	23	18	39	25	75
S	65	4	61	9	60	34	79	85	76	85
T	49	18	40	21	14	48	25	33	18	4
U	55	22	68	76	39	22	81	7	47	15
V	21	74	60	25	23	78	26	70	29	21
W	60	32	70	60	13	68	21	78	49	68
X	76	15	78	78	49	18	74	13	23	76
Y	78	9	81	36	70	26	60	18	70	29
Z	34	21	15	47	25	29	32	23	26	32

I	II	III	IV	V	VI	VII	VIII	IX	X

POSITION CHART

1	2	3	4	5
3, 4	7	8	0	2, 6
6	**7**	**8**	**9**	**10**
6	2	5	0	3
11	**12**	**13**	**14**	**15**
2, 7	1	0	4	0
16	**17**	**18**	**19**	**20**
2	1	0	7	5, 6
21	**22**	**23**	**24**	**25**
0	5	0	5, 8	0
26	**27**	**28**	**29**	**30**
0	1, 4	6	0	1
31	**32**	**33**	**34**	**35**
2	0	8	0	4
36	**37**	**38**	**39**	**40**
0	6	5	0	7
41	**42**	**43**	**44**	**45**
8	5	4	3	5
46	**47**	**48**	**49**	**50**
4	0	6, 7	0	4
51	**52**	**53**	**54**	**55**
3	2	7	8	0
56	**57**	**58**	**59**	**60**
6	5, 7	2	1	0
61	**62**	**63**	**64**	**65**
6	2	7	6	4
66	**67**	**68**	**69**	**70**
2, 8	1	0	3, 7	0
71	**72**	**73**	**74**	**75**
8	2, 4, 6	1, 3	0	3
76	**77**	**78**	**79**	**80**
0	3	0	1	8
81	**82**	**83**	**84**	**85**
0	1, 5	3	5	7

LETTERS MISSED

I. ——————————————————
 1 2 3 4 5 6 7 8

II. ——————————————————
 1 2 3 4 5 6 7 8

III. ——————————————
 1 2 3 4 5 6 7

IV. ——————————————
 1 2 3 4 5 6 7

V. ——————————————————
 1 2 3 4 5 6 7 8

VI. ——————————————————
 1 2 3 4 5 6 7 8

VII. ——————————————————
 1 2 3 4 5 6 7 8

VIII. ——————————————————
 1 2 3 4 5 6 7 8

IX. ——————————————
 1 2 3 4 5 6 7

X. ——————————————
 1 2 3 4 5 6 7

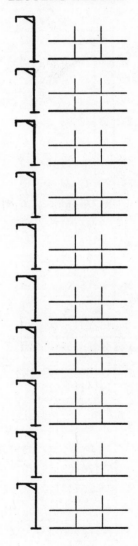

Par Score: 6

Your Score: _____

SOLITAIRE HANGMAN

LETTER CHART

	I	II	III	IV	V	VI	VII	VIII	IX	X
A	6	30	45	32	47	52	41	81	66	69
B	50	18	8	78	16	18	70	78	53	41
C	52	47	6	62	62	44	78	40	38	50
D	75	31	77	58	6	56	31	6	56	44
E	45	62	29	34	24	75	27	69	23	85
F	70	77	47	10	8	33	17	8	29	53
G	33	6	16	64	67	29	10	10	6	5
H	29	61	44	16	10	17	44	3	41	72
I	81	74	61	33	70	81	29	12	33	14
J	35	41	31	6	12	72	62	44	78	29
K	8	51	50	31	32	50	35	18	26	22
L	41	59	56	18	23	74	54	50	70	31
M	4	78	10	20	18	20	8	14	50	51
N	31	21	62	8	11	31	47	71	68	47
O	13	10	78	40	69	51	12	22	64	12
P	44	53	64	35	20	69	67	20	31	62
Q	10	33	18	41	22	22	22	53	67	40
R	64	44	2	53	5	65	74	29	20	81
S	32	64	12	44	40	35	57	9	13	56
T	38	49	20	84	29	8	16	67	44	64
U	74	34	70	11	44	76	72	31	35	61
V	53	70	22	22	72	41	53	74	8	33
W	56	35	40	29	31	10	18	33	62	6
X	62	50	33	47	33	64	64	35	47	8
Y	20	29	52	50	50	47	20	41	16	35
Z	47	8	30	12	35	53	50	16	72	74

	I	II	III	IV	V	VI	VII	VIII	IX	X

POSITION CHART

1	2	3	4	5
8	5, 7	2	3	4
6	**7**	**8**	**9**	**10**
0	8	0	4, 5	0
11	**12**	**13**	**14**	**15**
2	0	2	6	1, 3, 4
16	**17**	**18**	**19**	**20**
0	4	0	7, 8	0
21	**22**	**23**	**24**	**25**
4	0	7	6	4
26	**27**	**28**	**29**	**30**
3	2, 6	4	0	3
31	**32**	**33**	**34**	**35**
0	5	0	7	0
36	**37**	**38**	**39**	**40**
7	5	6	7	1
41	**42**	**43**	**44**	**45**
0	2	1	0	4
46	**47**	**48**	**49**	**50**
6	0	7	1	0
51	**52**	**53**	**54**	**55**
5	8	0	3, 5	5
56	**57**	**58**	**59**	**60**
0	1, 7, 8	4, 8	8	5
61	**62**	**63**	**64**	**65**
2	0	3, 6, 8	0	6
66	**67**	**68**	**69**	**70**
1, 4	0	5	3	0
71	**72**	**73**	**74**	**75**
8	0	3	0	1
76	**77**	**78**	**79**	**80**
2	6	0	1	1
81	**82**	**83**	**84**	**85**
7	3	1, 5	3, 6	8

LETTERS MISSED

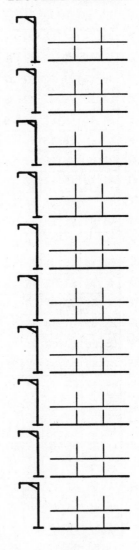

I. $\overline{\underset{1}{\quad}\underset{2}{\quad}\underset{3}{\quad}\underset{4}{\quad}\underset{5}{\quad}\underset{6}{\quad}\underset{7}{\quad}\underset{8}{\quad}}$

II. $\overline{\underset{1}{\quad}\underset{2}{\quad}\underset{3}{\quad}\underset{4}{\quad}\underset{5}{\quad}\underset{6}{\quad}\underset{7}{\quad}\underset{8}{\quad}}$

III. $\overline{\underset{1}{\quad}\underset{2}{\quad}\underset{3}{\quad}\underset{4}{\quad}\underset{5}{\quad}\underset{6}{\quad}\underset{7}{\quad}\underset{8}{\quad}}$

IV. $\overline{\underset{1}{\quad}\underset{2}{\quad}\underset{3}{\quad}\underset{4}{\quad}\underset{5}{\quad}\underset{6}{\quad}\underset{7}{\quad}\underset{8}{\quad}}$

V. $\overline{\underset{1}{\quad}\underset{2}{\quad}\underset{3}{\quad}\underset{4}{\quad}\underset{5}{\quad}\underset{6}{\quad}\underset{7}{\quad}}$

VI. $\overline{\underset{1}{\quad}\underset{2}{\quad}\underset{3}{\quad}\underset{4}{\quad}\underset{5}{\quad}\underset{6}{\quad}\underset{7}{\quad}\underset{8}{\quad}}$

VII. $\overline{\underset{1}{\quad}\underset{2}{\quad}\underset{3}{\quad}\underset{4}{\quad}\underset{5}{\quad}\underset{6}{\quad}\underset{7}{\quad}\underset{8}{\quad}}$

VIII. $\overline{\underset{1}{\quad}\underset{2}{\quad}\underset{3}{\quad}\underset{4}{\quad}\underset{5}{\quad}\underset{6}{\quad}\underset{7}{\quad}\underset{8}{\quad}}$

IX. $\overline{\underset{1}{\quad}\underset{2}{\quad}\underset{3}{\quad}\underset{4}{\quad}\underset{5}{\quad}\underset{6}{\quad}\underset{7}{\quad}}$

X. $\overline{\underset{1}{\quad}\underset{2}{\quad}\underset{3}{\quad}\underset{4}{\quad}\underset{5}{\quad}\underset{6}{\quad}\underset{7}{\quad}\underset{8}{\quad}}$

Par Score: 7

Your Score: ____

SOLITAIRE HANGMAN

LETTER CHART

	I	II	III	IV	V	VI	VII	VIII	IX	X
A	44	70	51	85	78	25	34	43	60	79
B	8	42	40	53	11	8	67	23	5	15
C	40	85	21	62	62	37	59	56	8	28
D	62	20	76	57	42	85	53	28	25	76
E	33	15	56	60	82	29	69	38	82	74
F	42	46	28	15	64	62	76	45	62	46
G	21	67	2	28	67	64	17	31	31	23
H	49	76	15	84	76	11	52	62	40	62
I	81	7	73	67	84	26	42	60	84	17
J	46	81	84	76	5	15	81	21	76	11
K	28	53	37	64	58	21	25	40	56	5
L	60	18	45	31	8	53	28	64	45	21
M	5	37	23	32	15	17	84	84	64	31
N	38	32	32	81	60	73	62	46	58	83
O	23	62	7	18	17	23	5	32	32	25
P	65	56	67	12	21	76	8	58	53	32
Q	84	58	46	56	32	28	32	53	11	81
R	64	17	83	70	27	55	23	6	15	8
S	35	8	81	35	23	67	11	76	67	35
T	10	51	17	58	1	81	49	67	21	85
U	53	35	35	8	25	84	15	81	17	37
V	17	5	25	5	35	56	64	5	23	40
W	37	59	42	11	28	32	37	8	81	53
X	56	40	53	21	40	58	21	11	28	42
Y	15	11	58	37	37	5	35	42	35	84
Z	11	64	62	17	81	35	40	15	83	56

| I | II | III | IV | V | VI | VII | VIII | IX | X |

POSITION CHART

1	2	3	4	5
3, 6	1	5	2, 8	0
6	**7**	**8**	**9**	**10**
3	2	0	6	8
11	**12**	**13**	**14**	**15**
0	4	1, 5, 6	7	0
16	**17**	**18**	**19**	**20**
5	0	3	5	4
21	**22**	**23**	**24**	**25**
0	7	0	7	0
26	**27**	**28**	**29**	**30**
3	8	0	2, 6, 7	4
31	**32**	**33**	**34**	**35**
1	0	1, 3	6	0
36	**37**	**38**	**39**	**40**
6	0	7	3	0
41	**42**	**43**	**44**	**45**
2, 3	0	4	6	5, 6
46	**47**	**48**	**49**	**50**
0	1	3	5	8
51	**52**	**53**	**54**	**55**
7	2, 7	0	6	1, 8
56	**57**	**58**	**59**	**60**
0	7	0	1	2
61	**62**	**63**	**64**	**65**
1	0	5	0	4
66	**67**	**68**	**69**	**70**
2	0	2	3, 4	6
71	**72**	**73**	**74**	**75**
1	8	4	6, 7	2
76	**77**	**78**	**79**	**80**
0	2	1, 5	2, 4	3, 4
81	**82**	**83**	**84**	**85**
0	4, 7	3	0	5

BIG CRITTERS

LETTERS MISSED

I. __ __ __ __ __ __ __ __
  1 2 3 4 5 6 7 8

II. __ __ __ __ __ __ __
   1 2 3 4 5 6 7

III. __ __ __ __ __ __ __
    1 2 3 4 5 6 7

IV. __ __ __ __ __ __ __
   1 2 3 4 5 6 7

V. __ __ __ __ __ __ __ __
  1 2 3 4 5 6 7 8

VI. __ __ __ __ __ __ __ __
   1 2 3 4 5 6 7 8

VII. __ __ __ __ __ __ __
    1 2 3 4 5 6 7

VIII. __ __ __ __ __ __ __
     1 2 3 4 5 6 7

IX. __ __ __ __ __ __ __
   1 2 3 4 5 6 7

X. __ __ __ __ __ __ __
  1 2 3 4 5 6 7

Par Score: 8

Your Score: ____

SOLITAIRE HANGMAN

LETTER CHART

	I	II	III	IV	V	VI	VII	VIII	IX	X
A	53	46	27	12	32	29	24	60	42	74
B	79	14	38	27	84	76	46	6	74	46
C	67	45	46	32	79	71	79	53	12	51
D	84	34	71	83	44	61	6	46	66	57
E	78	4	67	29	52	84	22	43	25	76
F	71	44	76	20	28	44	67	57	46	6
G	6	6	42	57	51	67	84	24	14	12
H	28	12	49	15	6	79	17	32	20	53
I	74	22	77	43	24	78	57	44	54	71
J	44	32	84	71	34	27	61	61	38	61
K	26	74	34	74	20	49	14	14	24	68
L	57	17	44	6	29	56	78	82	67	14
M	32	71	12	17	42	12	38	27	17	24
N	24	20	24	76	38	32	12	49	73	36
O	2	7	79	42	45	6	36	38	10	40
P	61	57	66	47	22	57	50	75	34	38
Q	12	27	53	14	61	14	27	20	71	79
R	8	28	62	52	74	17	42	42	79	17
S	76	53	83	24	12	20	59	17	49	34
T	27	24	36	61	67	24	28	84	53	26
U	17	61	85	79	17	34	20	28	7	66
V	20	38	74	34	27	83	76	45	57	42
W	25	67	57	38	14	38	44	12	61	27
X	14	76	14	84	76	74	34	34	27	67
Y	38	42	61	44	46	42	49	67	76	84
Z	34	79	6	67	57	46	53	71	44	20

I	II	III	IV	V	VI	VII	VIII	IX	X

POSITION CHART

1	2	3	4	5
3	2, 6	1	2, 7	3, 5
6	**7**	**8**	**9**	**10**
0	4	7	6	8
11	**12**	**13**	**14**	**15**
2, 4, 7	0	6	0	6
16	**17**	**18**	**19**	**20**
6, 8	0	5, 7	7	0
21	**22**	**23**	**24**	**25**
7	5	7	0	5
26	**27**	**28**	**29**	**30**
8	0	1	2, 7	1
31	**32**	**33**	**34**	**35**
5	3	3	0	4
36	**37**	**38**	**39**	**40**
2	4	0	2	3, 6
41	**42**	**43**	**44**	**45**
2	0	4	0	6
46	**47**	**48**	**49**	**50**
0	5	1	0	3
51	**52**	**53**	**54**	**55**
4	8	0	1	6
56	**57**	**58**	**59**	**60**
5, 6	0	1, 4, 6	6, 7	5, 7
61	**62**	**63**	**64**	**65**
0	4, 5	8	3	5
66	**67**	**68**	**69**	**70**
7	0	1, 5	5	1, 6
71	**72**	**73**	**74**	**75**
0	7	2, 3, 6	0	2
76	**77**	**78**	**79**	**80**
0	3	4	0	2
81	**82**	**83**	**84**	**85**
2	8	1	0	6

LETTERS MISSED

I. __ __ __ __ __ __ __ __
   1   2   3   4   5   6   7   8

II. __ __ __ __ __ __ __
   1   2   3   4   5   6   7

III. __ __ __ __ __ __ __
   1   2   3   4   5   6   7

IV. __ __ __ __ __ __ __ __
   1   2   3   4   5   6   7   8

V. __ __ __ __ __ __ __ __
   1   2   3   4   5   6   7   8

VI. __ __ __ __ __ __ __
   1   2   3   4   5   6   7

VII. __ __ __ __ __ __ __
   1   2   3   4   5   6   7

VIII. __ __ __ __ __ __ __ __
   1   2   3   4   5   6   7   8

IX. __ __ __ __ __ __ __ __
   1   2   3   4   5   6   7   8

X. __ __ __ __ __ __ __ __
   1   2   3   4   5   6   7   8

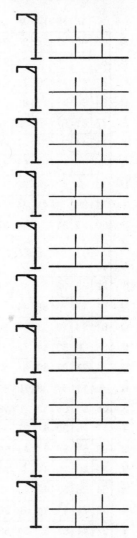

Par Score: 7

Your Score: ___

SOLITAIRE HANGMAN

LETTER CHART

	I	II	III	IV	V	VI	VII	VIII	IX	X
A	28	46	27	18	20	29	70	38	44	5
B	81	13	38	27	84	77	34	4	41	46
C	67	45	46	29	77	85	81	53	11	49
D	84	34	71	77	81	84	61	9	66	71
E	77	81	67	17	62	17	6	41	24	44
F	71	44	77	67	27	44	67	58	74	16
G	4	6	41	22	53	67	78	24	17	11
H	13	4	49	24	80	81	17	35	20	53
I	74	39	74	41	24	71	58	13	73	58
J	50	29	81	71	49	27	4	61	38	61
K	24	74	34	74	29	49	20	11	29	77
L	53	7	44	3	38	82	77	74	67	2
M	22	75	32	34	13	11	66	27	34	24
N	41	17	24	85	41	34	15	49	75	13
O	61	84	18	13	44	62	11	39	4	67
P	54	60	53	49	17	54	46	67	22	38
Q	11	27	29	58	61	4	24	20	71	81
R	6	11	57	38	79	80	47	36	13	17
S	66	53	58	32	4	13	27	6	50	34
T	17	26	30	61	67	35	44	1	46	20
U	20	61	84	81	46	61	38	29	81	41
V	29	20	4	11	9	74	84	44	49	74
W	34	58	52	46	48	6	41	34	53	27
X	38	71	11	84	6	20	29	10	58	84
Y	27	41	61	53	34	58	49	46	27	4
Z	44	67	6	20	58	24	53	71	77	6

I II III IV V VI VII VIII IX X

POSITION CHART

1	2	3	4	5
3	2,5	1	0	1,4,7
6	**7**	**8**	**9**	**10**
0	4	7	6	8
11	**12**	**13**	**14**	**15**
0	6	0	6	2
16	**17**	**18**	**19**	**20**
3,6	0	2,4,7	7	0
21	**22**	**23**	**24**	**25**
7	5	7	0	5
26	**27**	**28**	**29**	**30**
8	0	2,4,6	0	1
31	**32**	**33**	**34**	**35**
5	3	3	0	4
36	**37**	**38**	**39**	**40**
2	4	0	1,5,7	2
41	**42**	**43**	**44**	**45**
0	2	4	0	6
46	**47**	**48**	**49**	**50**
0	5	1	0	3
51	**52**	**53**	**54**	**55**
4	8	0	1	6
56	**57**	**58**	**59**	**60**
1,5,7	5,6	0	3,4	3
61	**62**	**63**	**64**	**65**
0	3,5,7	8	3	5
66	**67**	**68**	**69**	**70**
7	0	3,5,7	5	1,3,6
71	**72**	**73**	**74**	**75**
0	7	1,4,6	0	2
76	**77**	**78**	**79**	**80**
1	0	4	4,8	2
81	**82**	**83**	**84**	**85**
0	8	1	0	6

LETTERS MISSED

I. —————————————
   1   2   3   4   5   6   7

II. —————————————
   1   2   3   4   5   6   7   8

III. —————————————
   1   2   3   4   5   6   7   8

IV. —————————————
   1   2   3   4   5   6   7

V. —————————————
   1   2   3   4   5   6   7   8

VI. —————————————
   1   2   3   4   5   6   7   8

VII. —————————————
   1   2   3   4   5   6   7

VIII. —————————————
   1   2   3   4   5   6   7   8

IX. —————————————
   1   2   3   4   5   6   7

X. —————————————
   1   2   3   4   5   6   7

Par Score: 7

Your Score: _____

SOLITAIRE HANGMAN

LETTER CHART

	I	II	III	IV	V	VI	VII	VIII	IX	X
A	17	35	42	57	4	38	81	19	62	18
B	13	19	17	19	72	42	70	82	30	64
C	54	21	7	61	13	32	76	67	32	19
D	42	69	31	21	59	46	11	33	76	57
E	4	43	1	47	30	72	72	62	59	23
F	24	23	67	53	84	7	38	76	82	30
G	46	26	38	84	42	61	61	65	19	53
H	55	76	44	38	9	63	13	80	42	9
I	2	13	36	42	69	54	19	79	78	21
J	21	2	65	70	76	53	26	21	64	7
K	53	84	61	26	61	57	63	84	61	69
L	44	70	9	82	32	83	15	54	84	32
M	67	30	76	39	16	55	69	13	4	13
N	61	78	26	16	26	65	52	57	27	38
O	81	46	46	62	82	18	37	70	26	58
P	63	7	13	44	77	60	30	2	13	26
Q	7	36	84	23	7	84	21	61	2	82
R	52	80	22	30	52	67	77	30	57	72
S	15	10	53	46	46	26	67	59	34	84
T	49	42	19	69	63	70	7	26	44	44
U	19	34	55	66	19	44	82	23	53	2
V	65	67	6	55	53	76	42	34	63	55
W	57	82	70	13	21	82	53	72	7	61
X	30	32	21	32	44	19	44	9	38	42
Y	70	44	23	7	81	2	80	32	46	63
Z	9	38	72	63	55	9	84	42	55	56
	I	II	III	IV	V	VI	VII	VIII	IX	X

POSITION CHART

1	2	3	4	5
4, 7	0	2	4	6

6	7	8	9	10
3	0	3	0	1

11	12	13	14	15
4	2	0	1	7

16	17	18	19	20
5	6	2, 7	0	8

21	22	23	24	25
0	1, 5	0	1	5

26	27	28	29	30
0	6	7	1, 6, 7	0

31	32	33	34	35
8	0	1	3	4

36	37	38	39	40
2	5	0	1, 3, 8	3, 7

41	42	43	44	45
5, 8	0	7	0	2

46	47	48	49	50
0	4	4	8	4

51	52	53	54	55
8	3	0	5	0

56	57	58	59	60
3	0	4, 5	7	6, 8

61	62	63	64	65
0	2	0	1	0

66	67	68	69	70
7	0	5	6	0

71	72	73	74	75
3	0	4, 6, 7	6	7

76	77	78	79	80
0	1	5	4, 6	8

81	82	83	84	85
2	0	1, 3, 4	0	6

LETTERS MISSED

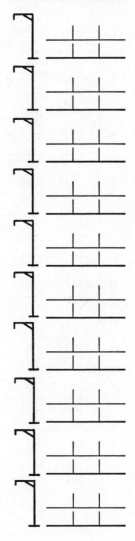

I. $\overline{}_1 \overline{}_2 \overline{}_3 \overline{}_4 \overline{}_5 \overline{}_6 \overline{}_7 \overline{}_8$

II. $\overline{}_1 \overline{}_2 \overline{}_3 \overline{}_4 \overline{}_5 \overline{}_6 \overline{}_7 \overline{}_8$

III. $\overline{}_1 \overline{}_2 \overline{}_3 \overline{}_4 \overline{}_5 \overline{}_6 \overline{}_7 \overline{}_8$

IV. $\overline{}_1 \overline{}_2 \overline{}_3 \overline{}_4 \overline{}_5 \overline{}_6 \overline{}_7 \overline{}_8$

V. $\overline{}_1 \overline{}_2 \overline{}_3 \overline{}_4 \overline{}_5 \overline{}_6 \overline{}_7$

VI. $\overline{}_1 \overline{}_2 \overline{}_3 \overline{}_4 \overline{}_5 \overline{}_6 \overline{}_7 \overline{}_8$

VII. $\overline{}_1 \overline{}_2 \overline{}_3 \overline{}_4 \overline{}_5 \overline{}_6 \overline{}_7 \overline{}_8$

VIII. $\overline{}_1 \overline{}_2 \overline{}_3 \overline{}_4 \overline{}_5 \overline{}_6 \overline{}_7 \overline{}_8$

IX. $\overline{}_1 \overline{}_2 \overline{}_3 \overline{}_4 \overline{}_5 \overline{}_6 \overline{}_7$

X. $\overline{}_1 \overline{}_2 \overline{}_3 \overline{}_4 \overline{}_5 \overline{}_6 \overline{}_7$

Par Score: 7

Your Score: ____

SOLITAIRE HANGMAN

LETTER CHART

	I	II	III	IV	V	VI	VII	VIII	IX	X
A	7	43	53	85	29	13	31	73	39	32
B	47	23	21	28	95	26	84	59	54	88
C	26	39	93	47	36	17	26	32	44	54
D	79	20	54	95	25	65	9	7	72	18
E	90	53	51	54	17	23	45	74	31	60
F	54	84	59	17	23	59	87	72	84	87
G	84	26	65	59	32	87	72	84	78	44
H	37	32	4	39	62	91	89	91	26	74
I	72	69	37	26	89	50	29	63	64	78
J	65	17	47	65	28	36	79	47	43	26
K	9	65	7	74	72	79	4	89	7	89
L	75	4	5	86	84	81	11	37	17	17
M	59	28	72	32	39	9	39	88	4	28
N	4	52	17	45	93	45	18	43	25	9
O	50	36	12	79	18	38	63	9	85	63
P	15	47	84	68	26	94	21	4	9	36
Q	43	54	87	72	43	84	65	79	12	23
R	36	87	9	23	47	72	47	17	30	81
S	91	33	14	36	66	68	95	31	74	14
T	35	35	35	43	9	4	54	12	65	42
U	68	7	89	84	63	7	28	87	89	72
V	74	59	32	87	54	89	7	23	29	79
W	28	91	79	9	59	74	32	54	79	84
X	17	72	74	4	4	12	74	65	23	39
Y	23	89	43	7	81	28	35	95	47	59
Z	12	9	23	89	87	32	43	26	87	47
	I	II	III	IV	V	VI	VII	VIII	IX	X

POSITION CHART

1	2	3	4	5
1, 9	10	2	0	3
6	**7**	**8**	**9**	**10**
9	0	2	0	2
11	**12**	**13**	**14**	**15**
3	0	5, 10	7	6
16	**17**	**18**	**19**	**20**
10	0	5	2	7
21	**22**	**23**	**24**	**25**
1	5	0	1	3
26	**27**	**28**	**29**	**30**
0	3, 7, 9	0	8	6, 10
31	**32**	**33**	**34**	**35**
9	0	3, 10	7	4
36	**37**	**38**	**39**	**40**
0	5	8	0	7
41	**42**	**43**	**44**	**45**
4	10	0	1	6
46	**47**	**48**	**49**	**50**
10	0	6	9	2, 7
51	**52**	**53**	**54**	**55**
8	6	2, 9	0	6
56	**57**	**58**	**59**	**60**
8	9	5	0	6, 8
61	**62**	**63**	**64**	**65**
2, 5	1	2	7	0
66	**67**	**68**	**69**	**70**
4	2	3	5, 8	5
71	**72**	**73**	**74**	**75**
5	0	4, 6, 8	0	8
76	**77**	**78**	**79**	**80**
3	8	4	0	2, 5, 7
81	**82**	**83**	**84**	**85**
9	4	10	0	2, 5
86	**87**	**88**	**89**	**90**
1, 4	0	3	0	9
91	**92**	**93**	**94**	**95**
1	1	6	4	7

AROUND THE WORLD

LETTERS MISSED

I. ___ ___ ___ ___ ___ ___ ___ ___ ___
    1 2 3 4 5 6 7 8 9

II. ___ ___ ___ ___ ___ ___ ___ ___ ___ ___
    1 2 3 4 5 6 7 8 9 10

III. ___ ___ ___ ___ ___ ___ ___ ___ ___
    1 2 3 4 5 6 7 8 9

IV. ___ ___ ___ ___ ___ ___ ___
    1 2 3 4 5 6 7

V. ___ ___ ___ ___ ___ ___ ___ ___ ___
    1 2 3 4 5 6 7 8 9

VI. ___ ___ ___ ___ ___ ___ ___ ___ ___ ___
    1 2 3 4 5 6 7 8 9 10

VII. ___ ___ ___ ___ ___ ___ ___ ___ ___
    1 2 3 4 5 6 7 8 9

VIII. ___ ___ ___ ___ ___ ___ ___ ___ ___
    1 2 3 4 5 6 7 8 9

IX. ___ ___ ___ ___ ___ ___ ___ ___ ___ ___
    1 2 3 4 5 6 7 8 9 10

X. ___ ___ ___ ___ ___ ___ ___ ___ ___ ___
    1 2 3 4 5 6 7 8 9 10

Par Score: 7

Your Score: _____

SOLITAIRE HANGMAN

LETTER CHART

	I	II	III	IV	V	VI	VII	VIII	IX	X
A	64	59	7	9	82	64	83	44	66	10
B	29	57	41	68	15	68	57	24	18	60
C	6	68	81	32	85	41	17	53	82	14
D	47	76	74	5	57	15	47	64	20	72
E	25	72	71	65	78	19	63	22	28	47
F	13	47	24	15	60	57	34	49	60	64
G	34	40	5	13	84	20	74	5	22	36
H	81	73	20	24	64	43	20	16	79	11
I	5	26	28	47	44	5	82	36	81	82
J	68	64	49	34	79	60	29	29	13	49
K	15	70	57	20	81	70	13	33	84	15
L	7	62	79	84	68	47	52	57	5	22
M	84	49	34	38	5	72	49	35	15	70
N	40	60	64	19	25	26	4	60	75	61
O	75	82	14	22	6	21	79	48	6	57
P	18	24	10	64	47	59	15	68	59	68
Q	14	13	68	41	22	74	76	20	68	18
R	20	41	21	70	18	33	14	38	57	13
S	70	81	70	18	35	44	81	12	70	74
T	54	44	26	6	13	6	33	26	24	63
U	82	28	72	76	52	16	5	6	47	76
V	22	74	12	10	20	4	24	70	29	79
W	57	34	76	60	34	76	6	79	41	20
X	41	15	47	74	49	84	18	72	26	81
Y	49	79	60	49	70	29	84	15	49	16
Z	36	5	85	36	24	79	64	47	34	24
	I	II	III	IV	V	VI	VII	VIII	IX	X

POSITION CHART

1 2, 3	**2** 7	**3** 8	**4** 6	**5** 0
6 0	**7** 2	**8** 5	**9** 2, 6	**10** 3
11 1, 8	**12** 1	**13** 0	**14** 4	**15** 0
16 2	**17** 1	**18** 0	**19** 7	**20** 0
21 5	**22** 0	**23** 4, 6, 8	**24** 0	**25** 1, 6
26 0	**27** 5, 7	**28** 6	**29** 0	**30** 3, 7, 8
31 2	**32** 1	**33** 8	**34** 0	**35** 4
36 0	**37** 6	**38** 5	**39** 1	**40** 7
41 0	**42** 5	**43** 4	**44** 3	**45** 5
46 4	**47** 0	**48** 6	**49** 0	**50** 2, 8
51 3	**52** 2	**53** 7	**54** 8	**55** 4
56 6	**57** 0	**58** 2	**59** 1	**60** 0
61 6	**62** 2	**63** 7	**64** 0	**65** 4
66 2, 4, 7	**67** 1	**68** 0	**69** 1, 5	**70** 0
71 8	**72** 0	**73** 4, 8	**74** 0	**75** 3
76 0	**77** 3	**78** 8	**79** 0	**80** 8
81 0	**82** 5	**83** 3	**84** 0	**85** 7

LETTERS MISSED

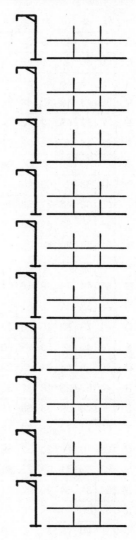

I. $\overline{\underset{1}{\quad}\ \underset{2}{\quad}\ \underset{3}{\quad}\ \underset{4}{\quad}\ \underset{5}{\quad}\ \underset{6}{\quad}\ \underset{7}{\quad}\ \underset{8}{\quad}}$

II. $\overline{\underset{1}{\quad}\ \underset{2}{\quad}\ \underset{3}{\quad}\ \underset{4}{\quad}\ \underset{5}{\quad}\ \underset{6}{\quad}\ \underset{7}{\quad}\ \underset{8}{\quad}}$

III. $\overline{\underset{1}{\quad}\ \underset{2}{\quad}\ \underset{3}{\quad}\ \underset{4}{\quad}\ \underset{5}{\quad}\ \underset{6}{\quad}\ \underset{7}{\quad}\ \underset{8}{\quad}}$

IV. $\overline{\underset{1}{\quad}\ \underset{2}{\quad}\ \underset{3}{\quad}\ \underset{4}{\quad}\ \underset{5}{\quad}\ \underset{6}{\quad}\ \underset{7}{\quad}}$

V. $\overline{\underset{1}{\quad}\ \underset{2}{\quad}\ \underset{3}{\quad}\ \underset{4}{\quad}\ \underset{5}{\quad}\ \underset{6}{\quad}\ \underset{7}{\quad}\ \underset{8}{\quad}}$

VI. $\overline{\underset{1}{\quad}\ \underset{2}{\quad}\ \underset{3}{\quad}\ \underset{4}{\quad}\ \underset{5}{\quad}\ \underset{6}{\quad}\ \underset{7}{\quad}\ \underset{8}{\quad}}$

VII. $\overline{\underset{1}{\quad}\ \underset{2}{\quad}\ \underset{3}{\quad}\ \underset{4}{\quad}\ \underset{5}{\quad}\ \underset{6}{\quad}\ \underset{7}{\quad}\ \underset{8}{\quad}}$

VIII. $\overline{\underset{1}{\quad}\ \underset{2}{\quad}\ \underset{3}{\quad}\ \underset{4}{\quad}\ \underset{5}{\quad}\ \underset{6}{\quad}\ \underset{7}{\quad}\ \underset{8}{\quad}}$

IX. $\overline{\underset{1}{\quad}\ \underset{2}{\quad}\ \underset{3}{\quad}\ \underset{4}{\quad}\ \underset{5}{\quad}\ \underset{6}{\quad}\ \underset{7}{\quad}}$

X. $\overline{\underset{1}{\quad}\ \underset{2}{\quad}\ \underset{3}{\quad}\ \underset{4}{\quad}\ \underset{5}{\quad}\ \underset{6}{\quad}\ \underset{7}{\quad}\ \underset{8}{\quad}}$

Par Score: **7**

Your Score: _____

SOLITAIRE HANGMAN

LETTER CHART

	I	II	III	IV	V	VI	VII	VIII	IX	X
A	21	2	43	80	36	27	75	4	69	30
B	59	36	39	78	83	2	1	54	78	35
C	76	23	15	82	59	31	78	78	10	45
D	36	48	18	10	44	26	80	59	80	15
E	4	57	53	12	76	8	59	44	8	61
F	48	15	42	63	26	59	39	63	15	78
G	20	39	36	35	61	48	8	80	58	20
H	47	83	8	69	15	42	18	36	54	36
I	25	80	46	27	50	11	54	39	48	48
J	26	8	63	83	48	78	36	2	59	42
K	61	26	20	48	39	35	20	8	83	63
L	71	56	26	2	80	4	73	61	23	26
M	65	44	29	29	18	44	42	73	36	29
N	39	38	11	9	51	54	26	23	50	67
O	31	73	80	15	28	23	27	83	84	9
P	78	42	2	50	53	80	64	10	44	54
Q	50	29	44	54	2	29	10	52	20	2
R	44	67	23	18	42	36	53	48	2	59
S	8	78	59	38	63	15	63	42	18	18
T	63	74	74	25	38	72	31	25	26	31
U	29	18	50	20	31	69	69	14	29	37
V	83	63	31	59	78	83	83	29	42	39
W	54	31	54	26	29	77	2	69	61	50
X	69	10	61	8	70	10	15	18	39	44
Y	2	20	78	31	20	39	29	50	43	66
Z	42	50	48	42	54	18	61	20	52	8

| | I | II | III | IV | V | VI | VII | VIII | IX | X |

POSITION CHART

1 / 5	**2** / 0	**3** / 3, 5	**4** / 3	**5** / 6
6 / 4, 7	**7** / 1, 8	**8** / 0	**9** / 3	**10** / 0
11 / 2	**12** / 2, 4	**13** / 1	**14** / 2, 6	**15** / 0
16 / 1, 6	**17** / 3	**18** / 0	**19** / 2	**20** / 0
21 / 7	**22** / 1	**23** / 4	**24** / 3	**25** / 5
26 / 0	**27** / 6	**28** / 4	**29** / 0	**30** / 5
31 / 0	**32** / 4	**33** / 5	**34** / 6	**35** / 1
36 / 0	**37** / 2	**38** / 8	**39** / 0	**40** / 8
41 / 4	**42** / 0	**43** / 7	**44** / 0	**45** / 7
46 / 1, 6	**47** / 2	**48** / 0	**49** / 4	**50** / 0
51 / 5, 7	**52** / 1	**53** / 3	**54** / 0	**55** / 3
56 / 2	**57** / 1, 3	**58** / 6	**59** / 0	**60** / 8
61 / 0	**62** / 2, 8	**63** / 0	**64** / 1	**65** / 4
66 / 4, 8	**67** / 6	**68** / 8	**69** / 0	**70** / 2
71 / 8	**72** / 7, 8	**73** / 7	**74** / 5	**75** / 2, 4, 8
76 / 1, 6	**77** / 5	**78** / 0	**79** / 7	**80** / 0
81 / 1	**82** / 7	**83** / 0	**84** / 2, 3, 5	**85** / 6

LETTERS MISSED

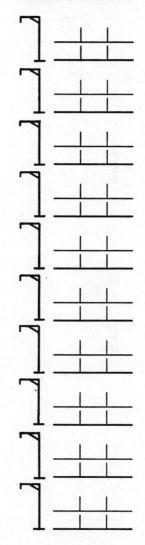

I. $\overline{}$ $\overline{}$ $\overline{}$ $\overline{}$ $\overline{}$ $\overline{}$ $\overline{}$ $\overline{}$
   1 2 3 4 5 6 7 8

II. 1 2 3 4 5 6 7 8

III. 1 2 3 4 5 6 7

IV. 1 2 3 4 5 6 7 8

V. 1 2 3 4 5 6 7 8

VI. 1 2 3 4 5 6 7 8

VII. 1 2 3 4 5 6 7 8

VIII. 1 2 3 4 5 6 7

IX. 1 2 3 4 5 6 7

X. 1 2 3 4 5 6 7 8

Par Score: 7

Your Score: _____

SOLITAIRE HANGMAN

LETTER CHART

	I	II	III	IV	V	VI	VII	VIII	IX	X
A	81	83	60	48	10	71	31	42	54	26
B	65	71	20	5	46	83	17	22	62	24
C	7	62	57	64	83	5	41	61	20	65
D	35	5	14	39	55	7	78	69	57	46
E	49	68	51	7	57	11	20	17	46	13
F	53	35	49	11	65	20	69	13	36	74
G	39	20	53	62	75	13	5	74	55	60
H	60	63	21	36	5	17	61	83	53	83
I	30	75	71	20	13	84	9	57	39	37
J	5	43	5	76	20	22	28	20	41	22
K	46	28	74	45	7	28	80	31	69	17
L	69	12	32	41	11	31	51	58	76	36
M	41	41	31	13	41	46	36	5	11	43
N	23	7	59	74	74	79	66	28	74	11
O	78	13	19	9	67	23	34	4	83	5
P	55	65	63	75	56	27	39	75	5	28
Q	62	46	22	49	43	36	60	62	43	7
R	80	69	28	83	22	39	7	36	7	75
S	75	74	36	17	14	41	62	71	13	14
T	28	53	17	79	48	19	74	65	17	49
U	66	22	62	43	28	14	11	39	49	52
V	51	11	7	22	31	43	63	41	22	31
W	83	31	58	46	60	49	75	7	21	62
X	36	45	65	28	69	63	83	11	63	39
Y	43	36	83	31	17	51	43	27	2	41
Z	57	39	69	60	36	65	53	43	28	20

	I	II	III	IV	V	VI	VII	VIII	IX	X

POSITION CHART

1	2	3	4	5
4	3, 7	4	7	0

6	7	8	9	10
7	0	5	6	6

11	12	13	14	15
0	2, 7	0	1	6

16	17	18	19	20
1	0	4, 6, 7	2	0

21	22	23	24	25
5	0	3	3, 6	6

26	27	28	29	30
8	4	0	8	2

31	32	33	34	35
0	7, 8	8	2, 3	1

36	37	38	39	40
0	7	1	0	7

41	42	43	44	45
0	2	0	5	4

46	47	48	49	50
0	2, 7, 8	2	0	2

51	52	53	54	55
0	2, 4	0	2, 4, 6	0

56	57	58	59	60
4, 7	0	3	4	0

61	62	63	64	65
1	0	0	3	0

66	67	68	69	70
7	3	3, 8	0	3

71	72	73	74	75
6	3	2	0	5

76	77	78	79	80
1	5	4	7	8

81	82	83	84	85
6	8	0	5	2, 3, 5

LETTERS MISSED

I. — — — — — — — —
  1   2   3   4   5   6   7   8

II. — — — — — — — —
  1   2   3   4   5   6   7   8

III. — — — — — — — —
  1   2   3   4   5   6   7   8

IV. — — — — — — —
  1   2   3   4   5   6   7

V. — — — — — — —
  1   2   3   4   5   6   7

VI. — — — — — — —
  1   2   3   4   5   6   7

VII. — — — — — — — —
  1   2   3   4   5   6   7   8

VIII. — — — — — — —
  1   2   3   4   5   6   7

IX. — — — — — — —
  1   2   3   4   5   6   7

X. — — — — — — — —
  1   2   3   4   5   6   7   8

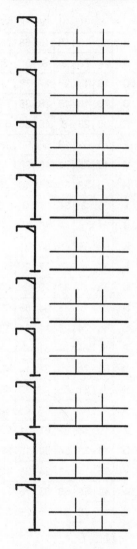

Par Score: 6

Your Score: ____

SOLITAIRE HANGMAN

LETTER CHART

	I	II	III	IV	V	VI	VII	VIII	IX	X
A	48	19	48	3	68	26	68	3	25	12
B	74	73	3	8	58	3	74	32	65	81
C	16	40	24	77	73	14	73	77	33	14
D	73	48	15	28	36	74	24	48	3	58
E	36	23	8	45	66	65	80	67	21	8
F	75	62	19	58	62	28	75	8	58	31
G	40	75	71	40	26	5	65	14	24	62
H	65	28	36	14	48	17	8	73	68	56
I	25	3	34	62	8	75	10	26	64	24
J	31	14	40	15	19	8	52	28	8	45
K	62	36	45	65	31	15	64	31	14	36
L	67	5	85	52	29	31	3	75	30	40
M	58	46	33	19	3	40	21	17	31	48
N	24	8	39	64	65	50	33	33	15	52
O	66	74	21	11	24	46	19	15	46	3
P	3	24	14	31	74	33	28	68	40	65
Q	68	26	26	21	14	58	45	36	62	68
R	79	31	65	48	79	45	4	1	10	55
S	8	45	73	68	45	52	37	21	73	15
T	19	53	52	67	41	25	83	24	57	75
U	14	33	64	80	15	39	48	11	19	44
V	26	15	28	24	21	48	26	40	26	19
W	45	58	58	33	75	73	15	45	45	73
X	15	68	31	75	28	62	31	52	75	26
Y	21	52	75	26	33	19	58	65	28	21
Z	28	21	62	73	12	24	14	19	36	33
	I	II	III	IV	V	VI	VII	VIII	IX	X

POSITION CHART

1	2	3	4	5
8	1	0	2	4
6	**7**	**8**	**9**	**10**
3, 6	8	0	2	3
11	**12**	**13**	**14**	**15**
2, 4	5	2, 7	0	0
16	**17**	**18**	**19**	**20**
4, 5	5	1	0	1
21	**22**	**23**	**24**	**25**
0	4	3, 5, 8	0	8
26	**27**	**28**	**29**	**30**
0	5	0	7	6, 7
31	**32**	**33**	**34**	**35**
0	6	0	2, 6, 8	1, 5
36	**37**	**38**	**39**	**40**
0	4	7	3, 7	0
41	**42**	**43**	**44**	**45**
4	7	6	3	0
46	**47**	**48**	**49**	**50**
2	6	0	7	6
51	**52**	**53**	**54**	**55**
3	0	6, 7	6	1, 6
56	**57**	**58**	**59**	**60**
2	1, 4	0	8	3
61	**62**	**63**	**64**	**65**
8	0	2	5	0
66	**67**	**68**	**69**	**70**
3, 6	7	0	4	3
71	**72**	**73**	**74**	**75**
4	5	0	1	0
76	**77**	**78**	**79**	**80**
1	1, 3	4, 8	2	6
81	**82**	**83**	**84**	**85**
4, 7	3	7	5	1

MORE FOOD FOR THOUGHT

LETTERS MISSED

I. $\overline{}$ $\underset{1}{}$ $\underset{2}{}$ $\underset{3}{}$ $\underset{4}{}$ $\underset{5}{}$ $\underset{6}{}$ $\underset{7}{}$ $\underset{8}{}$

II. $\underset{1}{}$ $\underset{2}{}$ $\underset{3}{}$ $\underset{4}{}$ $\underset{5}{}$ $\underset{6}{}$ $\underset{7}{}$ $\underset{8}{}$

III. $\underset{1}{}$ $\underset{2}{}$ $\underset{3}{}$ $\underset{4}{}$ $\underset{5}{}$ $\underset{6}{}$ $\underset{7}{}$ $\underset{8}{}$

IV. $\underset{1}{}$ $\underset{2}{}$ $\underset{3}{}$ $\underset{4}{}$ $\underset{5}{}$ $\underset{6}{}$ $\underset{7}{}$

V. $\underset{1}{}$ $\underset{2}{}$ $\underset{3}{}$ $\underset{4}{}$ $\underset{5}{}$ $\underset{6}{}$ $\underset{7}{}$

VI. $\underset{1}{}$ $\underset{2}{}$ $\underset{3}{}$ $\underset{4}{}$ $\underset{5}{}$ $\underset{6}{}$ $\underset{7}{}$ $\underset{8}{}$

VII. $\underset{1}{}$ $\underset{2}{}$ $\underset{3}{}$ $\underset{4}{}$ $\underset{5}{}$ $\underset{6}{}$ $\underset{7}{}$

VIII. $\underset{1}{}$ $\underset{2}{}$ $\underset{3}{}$ $\underset{4}{}$ $\underset{5}{}$ $\underset{6}{}$ $\underset{7}{}$ $\underset{8}{}$

IX. $\underset{1}{}$ $\underset{2}{}$ $\underset{3}{}$ $\underset{4}{}$ $\underset{5}{}$ $\underset{6}{}$ $\underset{7}{}$ $\underset{8}{}$

X. $\underset{1}{}$ $\underset{2}{}$ $\underset{3}{}$ $\underset{4}{}$ $\underset{5}{}$ $\underset{6}{}$ $\underset{7}{}$

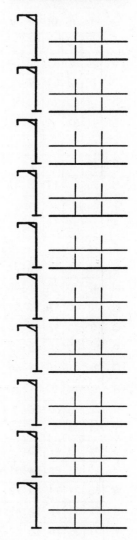

Par Score: 8

Your Score: _____

SOLITAIRE HANGMAN

LETTER CHART

	I	II	III	IV	V	VI	VII	VIII	IX	X
A	3	19	10	65	6	35	81	64	58	43
B	68	5	43	83	64	79	49	29	47	10
C	6	43	64	47	52	70	26	51	62	64
D	14	64	70	64	68	83	54	43	10	83
E	61	37	1	39	54	62	78	11	14	7
F	49	29	72	58	19	21	12	26	64	45
G	43	47	14	5	51	12	64	68	19	68
H	56	54	19	10	47	10	29	31	54	5
I	64	1	26	51	25	14	5	57	6	47
J	70	83	31	43	21	43	45	45	28	14
K	19	72	82	79	58	5	68	5	17	21
L	54	25	15	68	37	45	18	10	5	81
M	47	10	5	2	26	22	70	38	43	19
N	16	70	17	76	56	64	76	25	26	76
O	5	79	37	18	14	82	19	66	57	79
P	83	49	29	45	83	54	48	47	29	13
Q	21	21	21	49	49	19	72	70	31	74
R	74	14	45	61	10	24	40	17	83	4
S	26	58	60	56	5	36	14	4	39	49
T	51	42	6	26	43	68	10	14	30	26
U	45	28	47	70	29	26	47	76	51	58
V	29	45	68	54	31	47	31	19	45	31
W	58	31	74	19	72	29	51	21	21	51
X	72	51	49	72	45	58	43	72	49	37
Y	31	26	76	40	42	31	8	49	56	54
Z	76	44	79	74	70	49	58	74	68	29
	I	II	III	IV	V	VI	VII	VIII	IX	X

POSITION CHART

1 — 3, 5	**2** — 5	**3** — 4	**4** — 3	**5** — 0
6 — 6	**7** — 2, 6	**8** — 3	**9** — 3	**10** — 0
11 — 7	**12** — 1	**13** — 1, 4	**14** — 0	**15** — 4
16 — 2, 5	**17** — 8	**18** — 2	**19** — 0	**20** — 1
21 — 0	**22** — 6	**23** — 3, 5	**24** — 8	**25** — 4
26 — 0	**27** — 5	**28** — 1	**29** — 0	**30** — 5
31 — 0	**32** — 1	**33** — 8	**34** — 1	**35** — 5
36 — 3, 4	**37** — 7	**38** — 1, 6	**39** — 4	**40** — 8
41 — 8	**42** — 2	**43** — 0	**44** — 6	**45** — 0
46 — 6	**47** — 0	**48** — 4, 6	**49** — 0	**50** — 4, 7, 8
51 — 0	**52** — 1, 5	**53** — 6	**54** — 0	**55** — 4
56 — 3	**57** — 2	**58** — 0	**59** — 4	**60** — 1
61 — 1, 7	**62** — 7	**63** — 7	**64** — 0	**65** — 6
66 — 5	**67** — 2	**68** — 0	**69** — 2, 6, 7	**70** — 0
71 — 3	**72** — 0	**73** — 7	**74** — 0	**75** — 6, 8
76 — 0	**77** — 3	**78** — 7	**79** — 0	**80** — 3, 5, 7
81 — 5	**82** — 2	**83** — 0	**84** — 2	**85** — 4, 5

LETTERS MISSED

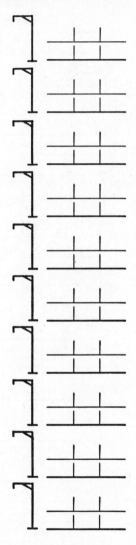

I. $\overline{}\ \overline{}\ \overline{}\ \overline{}\ \overline{}\ \overline{}\ \overline{}$
1 2 3 4 5 6 7

II. $\overline{}\ \overline{}\ \overline{}\ \overline{}\ \overline{}\ \overline{}\ \overline{}$
1 2 3 4 5 6 7

III. $\overline{}\ \overline{}\ \overline{}\ \overline{}\ \overline{}\ \overline{}\ \overline{}\ \overline{}$
1 2 3 4 5 6 7 8

IV. $\overline{}\ \overline{}\ \overline{}\ \overline{}\ \overline{}\ \overline{}\ \overline{}\ \overline{}$
1 2 3 4 5 6 7 8

V. $\overline{}\ \overline{}\ \overline{}\ \overline{}\ \overline{}\ \overline{}\ \overline{}$
1 2 3 4 5 6 7

VI. $\overline{}\ \overline{}\ \overline{}\ \overline{}\ \overline{}\ \overline{}\ \overline{}\ \overline{}$
1 2 3 4 5 6 7 8

VII. $\overline{}\ \overline{}\ \overline{}\ \overline{}\ \overline{}\ \overline{}\ \overline{}\ \overline{}$
1 2 3 4 5 6 7 8

VIII. $\overline{}\ \overline{}\ \overline{}\ \overline{}\ \overline{}\ \overline{}\ \overline{}\ \overline{}$
1 2 3 4 5 6 7 8

IX. $\overline{}\ \overline{}\ \overline{}\ \overline{}\ \overline{}\ \overline{}\ \overline{}\ \overline{}$
1 2 3 4 5 6 7 8

X. $\overline{}\ \overline{}\ \overline{}\ \overline{}\ \overline{}\ \overline{}\ \overline{}$
1 2 3 4 5 6 7

Par Score: 6   Your Score: _____

SOLITAIRE HANGMAN

LETTER CHART

	I	II	III	IV	V	VI	VII	VIII	IX	X
A	21	19	79	16	53	24	85	48	57	74
B	55	51	39	57	7	69	42	7	39	64
C	32	79	20	11	34	71	27	65	73	7
D	62	71	32	7	35	51	51	63	77	39
E	53	5	65	14	11	10	32	59	53	19
F	39	7	34	34	1	83	76	62	27	59
G	45	62	42	20	62	64	14	57	11	79
H	27	22	16	19	76	30	34	30	59	71
I	7	55	55	45	36	33	28	3	21	77
J	71	36	14	47	42	62	73	75	7	42
K	73	39	36	71	27	73	62	34	16	14
L	13	64	82	22	82	79	57	71	75	45
M	69	77	11	69	71	25	75	11	29	36
N	79	57	62	75	79	75	7	79	20	34
O	51	82	22	18	49	11	82	77	2	11
P	78	73	57	27	20	7	16	26	13	27
Q	34	35	30	51	32	34	55	82	82	62
R	59	76	74	32	39	77	63	14	5	76
S	22	20	45	30	57	14	77	16	84	69
T	5	54	3	74	14	3	20	20	36	37
U	11	49	24	9	16	47	22	22	22	32
V	75	11	47	82	22	39	59	36	45	47
W	64	14	51	73	77	55	3	27	42	51
X	14	16	27	36	47	16	71	64	14	55
Y	67	75	59	42	75	82	54	69	32	82
Z	16	69	7	59	45	20	11	32	62	57

POSITION CHART

1	2	3	4	5
6, 7	7	5	3	6

6	7	8	9	10
1, 4, 7	0	1	3, 6	8

11	12	13	14	15
0	1	5	0	7

16	17	18	19	20
0	5	5	2	0

21	22	23	24	25
4	0	5	2	7

26	27	28	29	30
8	0	3	3	1

31	32	33	34	35
2, 4, 8	0	6	0	4

36	37	38	39	40
0	5, 6	3	0	8

41	42	43	44	45
6	0	6	8	0

46	47	48	49	50
4	0	2, 7	5	1, 3

51	52	53	54	55
0	8	2	7	0

56	57	58	59	60
2	0	3, 4, 8	0	1, 5

61	62	63	64	65
8	0	4	0	6

66	67	68	69	70
2	7	6	0	2

71	72	73	74	75
0	4	0	4, 7	0

76	77	78	79	80
1	0	1	3	3

81	82	83	84	85
7	0	4	1	2, 6

LETTERS MISSED

I. $\overline{}\ \overline{}\ \overline{}\ \overline{}\ \overline{}\ \overline{}\ \overline{}$
1 2 3 4 5 6 7

II. $\overline{}\ \overline{}\ \overline{}\ \overline{}\ \overline{}\ \overline{}\ \overline{}$
1 2 3 4 5 6 7

III. $\overline{}\ \overline{}\ \overline{}\ \overline{}\ \overline{}\ \overline{}\ \overline{}$
1 2 3 4 5 6 7

IV. $\overline{}\ \overline{}\ \overline{}\ \overline{}\ \overline{}\ \overline{}\ \overline{}$
1 2 3 4 5 6 7

V. $\overline{}\ \overline{}\ \overline{}\ \overline{}\ \overline{}\ \overline{}\ \overline{}$
1 2 3 4 5 6 7

VI. $\overline{}\ \overline{}\ \overline{}\ \overline{}\ \overline{}\ \overline{}\ \overline{}\ \overline{}$
1 2 3 4 5 6 7 8

VII. $\overline{}\ \overline{}\ \overline{}\ \overline{}\ \overline{}\ \overline{}\ \overline{}$
1 2 3 4 5 6 7

VIII. $\overline{}\ \overline{}\ \overline{}\ \overline{}\ \overline{}\ \overline{}\ \overline{}\ \overline{}$
1 2 3 4 5 6 7 8

IX. $\overline{}\ \overline{}\ \overline{}\ \overline{}\ \overline{}\ \overline{}\ \overline{}$
1 2 3 4 5 6 7

X. $\overline{}\ \overline{}\ \overline{}\ \overline{}\ \overline{}\ \overline{}\ \overline{}$
1 2 3 4 5 6 7

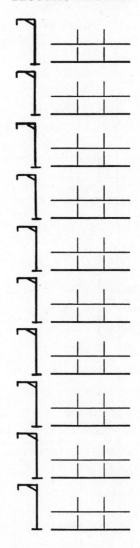

Par Score: 8

Your Score: _____

SOLITAIRE HANGMAN

LETTER CHART

	I	II	III	IV	V	VI	VII	VIII	IX	X
A	83	29	14	19	60	32	6	37	27	58
B	35	42	82	22	37	21	72	.9	32	22
C	15	62	22	36	55	57	4	6	82	52
D	43	82	6	51	22	41	15	51	37	66
E	3	4	32	6	40	63	37	13	15	20
F	22	80	17	80	32	72	82	78	9	41
G	66	77	51	9	46	59	9	54	71	78
H	5	49	57	82	51	69	11	35	22	6
I	26	54	81	57	33	26	79	62	25	69
J	57	51	29	11	26	78	57	69	66	29
K	69	69	78	59	29	80	22	57	26	26
L	4	32	15	33	45	33	51	22	51	45
M	29	59	43	29	66	62	26	80	69	72
N	72	48	33	46	57	82	78	59	53	82
O	9	3	80	72	34	8	18	4	41	4
P	54	15	72	69	79	46	29	15	78	34
Q	78	43	59	62	69	6	80	34	34	37
R	80	64	26	66	48	66	23	73	46	9
S	32	57	62	3	72	16	85	66	16	18
T	73	26	30	39	41	23	32	83	59	43
U	6	66	37	26	78	34	34	43	6	46
V	82	6	66	41	80	51	66	82	11	51
W	51	34	41	34	59	9	41	41	29	80
X	11	9	34	15	62	11	62	46	57	57
Y	59	22	27	18	82	15	69	32	72	32
Z	34	46	9	78	15	22	59	11	43	59

	I	II	III	IV	V	VI	VII	VIII	IX	X

POSITION CHART

1	2	3	4	5
7, 8	1	7	2	4
6	**7**	**8**	**9**	**10**
0	1	1, 4	0	1
11	**12**	**13**	**14**	**15**
0	4	4, 7	1	0
16	**17**	**18**	**19**	**20**
3	2, 3	6	2, 4	5, 8
21	**22**	**23**	**24**	**25**
2	0	7	6	1, 4, 7
26	**27**	**28**	**29**	**30**
0	8	3	0	7
31	**32**	**33**	**34**	**35**
3	0	5	0	6
36	**37**	**38**	**39**	**40**
1	0	7	3, 8	2
41	**42**	**43**	**44**	**45**
0	6	0	6	4
46	**47**	**48**	**49**	**50**
0	2	1	5	2
51	**52**	**53**	**54**	**55**
0	1, 7	2, 6	3	6
56	**57**	**58**	**59**	**60**
2	0	3	0	7
61	**62**	**63**	**64**	**65**
5	0	6, 8	8	5
66	**67**	**68**	**69**	**70**
0	4	8	0	8
71	**72**	**73**	**74**	**75**
5	0	8	4	7
76	**77**	**78**	**79**	**80**
5	4	0	3	0
81	**82**	**83**	**84**	**85**
4, 6	0	1, 5	8	1,4,5,8

LETTERS MISSED

I. $\overline{}_{1}\ \overline{}_{2}\ \overline{}_{3}\ \overline{}_{4}\ \overline{}_{5}\ \overline{}_{6}\ \overline{}_{7}\ \overline{}_{8}$

II. $\overline{}_{1}\ \overline{}_{2}\ \overline{}_{3}\ \overline{}_{4}\ \overline{}_{5}\ \overline{}_{6}\ \overline{}_{7}\ \overline{}_{8}$

III. $\overline{}_{1}\ \overline{}_{2}\ \overline{}_{3}\ \overline{}_{4}\ \overline{}_{5}\ \overline{}_{6}\ \overline{}_{7}\ \overline{}_{8}$

IV. $\overline{}_{1}\ \overline{}_{2}\ \overline{}_{3}\ \overline{}_{4}\ \overline{}_{5}\ \overline{}_{6}\ \overline{}_{7}\ \overline{}_{8}$

V. $\overline{}_{1}\ \overline{}_{2}\ \overline{}_{3}\ \overline{}_{4}\ \overline{}_{5}\ \overline{}_{6}\ \overline{}_{7}$

VI. $\overline{}_{1}\ \overline{}_{2}\ \overline{}_{3}\ \overline{}_{4}\ \overline{}_{5}\ \overline{}_{6}\ \overline{}_{7}\ \overline{}_{8}$

VII. $\overline{}_{1}\ \overline{}_{2}\ \overline{}_{3}\ \overline{}_{4}\ \overline{}_{5}\ \overline{}_{6}\ \overline{}_{7}\ \overline{}_{8}$

VIII. $\overline{}_{1}\ \overline{}_{2}\ \overline{}_{3}\ \overline{}_{4}\ \overline{}_{5}\ \overline{}_{6}\ \overline{}_{7}\ \overline{}_{8}$

IX. $\overline{}_{1}\ \overline{}_{2}\ \overline{}_{3}\ \overline{}_{4}\ \overline{}_{5}\ \overline{}_{6}\ \overline{}_{7}\ \overline{}_{8}$

X. $\overline{}_{1}\ \overline{}_{2}\ \overline{}_{3}\ \overline{}_{4}\ \overline{}_{5}\ \overline{}_{6}\ \overline{}_{7}\ \overline{}_{8}$

Par Score: 7

Your Score: _____

SOLITAIRE HANGMAN

LETTER CHART

	I	II	III	IV	V	VI	VII	VIII	IX	X
A	47	19	51	33	81	33	73	10	33	8
B	8	73	83	2	55	3	83	26	65	83
C	22	43	11	31	73	11	3	83	32	11
D	83	62	14	75	64	73	26	49	7	55
E	43	14	15	61	45	26	13	55	26	14
F	3	26	20	55	62	28	8	8	57	33
G	39	74	73	39	59	5	77	3	28	57
H	27	28	64	83	47	16	11	79	73	64
I	14	23	52	16	8	10	12	28	49	32
J	30	16	35	14	19	83	52	65	85	45
K	62	38	39	72	30	14	62	32	5	36
L	59	83	3	56	26	30	70	73	14	61
M	55	66	36	3	33	39	28	22	30	47
N	34	3	62	35	70	53	76	35	44	16
O	38	30	8	44	57	46	19	21	19	4
P	73	8	26	30	11	59	36	84	39	30
Q	67	11	28	8	83	62	45	36	62	52
R	11	32	68	40	79	45	16	11	38	49
S	26	45	16	52	49	52	32	85	83	19
T	19	39	70	57	39	24	30	14	11	5
U	79	35	47	65	3	67	47	45	4	81
V	28	47	19	11	65	47	35	39	16	3
W	35	40	55	32	28	8	14	16	45	35
X	57	67	30	73	32	49	39	52	67	26
Y	16	36	78	62	67	19	55	30	12	59
Z	32	49	32	19	14	55	40	67	3	28
	I	II	III	IV	V	VI	VII	VIII	IX	X

POSITION CHART

1 1, 4	**2** 1	**3** 0	**4** 2	**5** 4
6 7	**7** 8	**8** 0	**9** 2	**10** 3
11 0	**12** 5	**13** 2,7,8	**14** 0	**15** 2,6
16 0	**17** 5	**18** 1,3,6	**19** 0	**20** 1
21 6, 7	**22** 4	**23** 2, 5	**24** 8	**25** 8
26 0	**27** 5	**28** 0	**29** 1,7,8	**30** 0
31 4	**32** 0	**33** 6	**34** 3 ,8	**35** 0
36 0	**37** 6, 8	**38** 7	**39** 0	**40** 0
41 4	**42** 7	**43** 6	**44** 3	**45** 0
46 2	**47** 0	**48** 6	**49** 0	**50** 6
51 3	**52** 0	**53** 5, 7	**54** 6	**55** 0
56 2	**57** 0	**58** 7	**59** 1	**60** 3
61 8	**62** 0	**63** 2	**64** 5	**65** 0
66 3, 4	**67** 0	**68** 7	**69** 3	**70** 4
71 3	**72** 5	**73** 0	**74** 1	**75** 7
76 1	**77** 3, 6	**78** 8	**79** 2	**80** 6
81 3, 7	**82** 4	**83** 0	**84** 5	**85** 1

LETTERS MISSED

I. $\overline{}\ \overline{}\ \overline{}\ \overline{}\ \overline{}\ \overline{}\ \overline{}\ \overline{}$
1 2 3 4 5 6 7 8

II. $\overline{}\ \overline{}\ \overline{}\ \overline{}\ \overline{}\ \overline{}\ \overline{}$
1 2 3 4 5 6 7

III. $\overline{}\ \overline{}\ \overline{}\ \overline{}\ \overline{}\ \overline{}\ \overline{}\ \overline{}$
1 2 3 4 5 6 7 8

IV. $\overline{}\ \overline{}\ \overline{}\ \overline{}\ \overline{}\ \overline{}\ \overline{}\ \overline{}$
1 2 3 4 5 6 7 8

V. $\overline{}\ \overline{}\ \overline{}\ \overline{}\ \overline{}\ \overline{}\ \overline{}$
1 2 3 4 5 6 7

VI. $\overline{}\ \overline{}\ \overline{}\ \overline{}\ \overline{}\ \overline{}\ \overline{}\ \overline{}$
1 2 3 4 5 6 7 8

VII. $\overline{}\ \overline{}\ \overline{}\ \overline{}\ \overline{}\ \overline{}\ \overline{}\ \overline{}$
1 2 3 4 5 6 7 8

VIII. $\overline{}\ \overline{}\ \overline{}\ \overline{}\ \overline{}\ \overline{}\ \overline{}$
1 2 3 4 5 6 7

IX. $\overline{}\ \overline{}\ \overline{}\ \overline{}\ \overline{}\ \overline{}\ \overline{}\ \overline{}$
1 2 3 4 5 6 7 8

X. $\overline{}\ \overline{}\ \overline{}\ \overline{}\ \overline{}\ \overline{}\ \overline{}\ \overline{}$
1 2 3 4 5 6 7 8

Par Score: 6

Your Score: _____

165

SOLITAIRE HANGMAN

LETTER CHART

	I	II	III	IV	V	VI	VII	VIII	IX	X
A	79	43	32	22	16	36	16	10	18	79
B	47	24	8	47	47	75	27	4	5	7
C	81	27	83	8	23	27	36	33	33	83
D	49	79	65	70	33	56	65	7	81	16
E	40	65	34	71	42	49	25	5	19	56
F	36	36	53	23	81	59	42	21	34	82
G	7	51	40	21	39	4	7	59	79	45
H	24	81	21	39	61	79	66	24	51	39
I	39	59	36	37	35	21	21	61	16	67
J	83	68	4	42	21	44	59	42	83	53
K	42	53	24	51	49	24	83	16	66	33
L	51	61	68	44	45	39	35	27	21	22
M	16	73	16	79	66	42	24	39	4	11
N	5	21	5	72	83	16	50	79	47	59
O	85	64	85	49	78	85	81	44	7	85
P	11	83	51	53	46	68	61	13	82	81
Q	33	4	27	7	59	81	47	47	59	34
R	21	82	39	59	4	61	33	14	43	65
S	75	33	42	61	27	40	4	36	41	21
T	37	5	79	66	5	33	79	23	24	4
U	27	34	70	68	24	67	68	34	27	66
V	53	16	23	81	7	34	39	81	49	36
W	34	39	81	16	36	7	48	49	68	24
X	4	66	33	24	79	66	34	22	36	27
Y	44	42	66	83	44	58	80	43	76	68
Z	68	49	7	4	34	47	44	70	39	42
	I	II	III	IV	V	VI	VII	VIII	IX	X

POSITION CHART

1	2	3	4	5
1	8	2	0	7
6	**7**	**8**	**9**	**10**
8	0	5	8	2, 5
11	**12**	**13**	**14**	**15**
4	7	4	8	6
16	**17**	**18**	**19**	**20**
0	7	2	5	4
21	**22**	**23**	**24**	**25**
0	3	1	0	2, 7
26	**27**	**28**	**29**	**30**
5	0	6	7	5
31	**32**	**33**	**34**	**35**
7	2, 4	0	0	4
36	**37**	**38**	**39**	**40**
0	2	2	0	3
41	**42**	**43**	**44**	**45**
3, 4	0	6	0	5
46	**47**	**48**	**49**	**50**
3	0	3, 6	0	1
51	**52**	**53**	**54**	**55**
0	6	0 .	3	1
56	**57**	**58**	**59**	**60**
7	4	4, 8	0	3, 6, 7
61	**62**	**63**	**64**	**65**
0	3	6	2, 3	8
66	**67**	**68**	**69**	**70**
0	2	0	3	0
71	**72**	**73**	**74**	**75**
6, 7	4	4, 5	2	1, 5
76	**77**	**78**	**79**	**80**
8	1, 5	2, 6	0	5
81	**82**	**83**	**84**	**85**
0	1	0	1	6

IT TAKES ALL KINDS

LETTERS MISSED

I. $\overline{}$ $\overline{}$ $\overline{}$ $\overline{}$ $\overline{}$ $\overline{}$ $\overline{}$
   1   2   3   4   5   6   7

II. $\overline{}$ $\overline{}$ $\overline{}$ $\overline{}$ $\overline{}$ $\overline{}$ $\overline{}$ $\overline{}$
    1   2   3   4   5   6   7   8

III. $\overline{}$ $\overline{}$ $\overline{}$ $\overline{}$ $\overline{}$ $\overline{}$ $\overline{}$ $\overline{}$
     1   2   3   4   5   6   7   8

IV. $\overline{}$ $\overline{}$ $\overline{}$ $\overline{}$ $\overline{}$ $\overline{}$ $\overline{}$
     1   2   3   4   5   6   7

V. $\overline{}$ $\overline{}$ $\overline{}$ $\overline{}$ $\overline{}$ $\overline{}$ $\overline{}$
    1   2   3   4   5   6   7

VI. $\overline{}$ $\overline{}$ $\overline{}$ $\overline{}$ $\overline{}$ $\overline{}$ $\overline{}$ $\overline{}$
     1   2   3   4   5   6   7   8

VII. $\overline{}$ $\overline{}$ $\overline{}$ $\overline{}$ $\overline{}$ $\overline{}$ $\overline{}$ $\overline{}$
     1   2   3   4   5   6   7   8

VIII. $\overline{}$ $\overline{}$ $\overline{}$ $\overline{}$ $\overline{}$ $\overline{}$ $\overline{}$ $\overline{}$
      1   2   3   4   5   6   7   8

IX. $\overline{}$ $\overline{}$ $\overline{}$ $\overline{}$ $\overline{}$ $\overline{}$ $\overline{}$ $\overline{}$
     1   2   3   4   5   6   7   8

X. $\overline{}$ $\overline{}$ $\overline{}$ $\overline{}$ $\overline{}$ $\overline{}$ $\overline{}$ $\overline{}$
    1   2   3   4   5   6   7   8

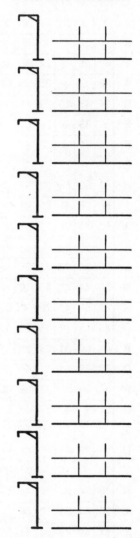

Par Score: 5

Your Score: _____

SOLITAIRE HANGMAN

LETTER CHART

	I	II	III	IV	V	VI	VII	VIII	IX	X
A	3	36	22	45	5	40	15	7	9	68
B	68	55	64	22	30	45	12	79	64	11
C	32	5	28	38	56	81	58	22	45	79
D	24	45	10	23	11	25	45	68	52	75
E	5	33	5	29	84	53	59	5	47	45
F	45	64	4	25	28	79	32	30	53	77
G	10	47	77	47	13	47	11	53	70	40
H	47	80	66	53	57	4	68	81	77	29
I	59	76	9	69	22	70	1	14	30	26
J	53	71	25	71	32	11	4	25	34	64
K	11	53	82	4	82	22	30	32	55	80
L	28	38	13	73	25	83	25	38	57	70
M	55	44	68	55	79	77	13	11	66	30
N	81	57	41	75	4	55	22	55	3	13
O	40	75	71	15	53	30	10	28	22	53
P	64	66	31	28	38	71	66	51	32	55
Q	73	73	11	11	64	38	47	45	68	4
R	57	22	30	13	29	33	3	58	85	66
S	85	4	38	57	47	57	60	74	82	15
T	4	49	73	30	65	13	53	82	38	5
U	66	32	53	82	68	68	73	57	26	22
V	25	68	75	64	71	82	79	77	24	32
W	13	77	27	32	45	64	28	71	71	47
X	30	25	32	80	66	32	64	13	28	71
Y	82	79	79	66	34	39	34	47	73	56
Z	22	82	34	1	55	66	38	64	4	82
	I	II	III	IV	V	VI	VII	VIII	IX	X

POSITION CHART

1	2	3	4	5
6	3, 8	3	0	8
6	**7**	**8**	**9**	**10**
6	2	3	2, 6	4
11	**12**	**13**	**14**	**15**
0	5	0	6	1
16	**17**	**18**	**19**	**20**
8	5	2	2, 5, 7	8
21	**22**	**23**	**24**	**25**
2	0	4	1	0
26	**27**	**28**	**29**	**30**
5	1	0	7	0
31	**32**	**33**	**34**	**35**
5, 7	0	3	0	1
36	**37**	**38**	**39**	**40**
5	3	0	2	6
41	**42**	**43**	**44**	**45**
3	7	6	4	0
46	**47**	**48**	**49**	**50**
2, 5, 8	0	4	1, 6	4
51	**52**	**53**	**54**	**55**
3, 4	8	0	8	0
56	**57**	**58**	**59**	**60**
3	0	7	2	8
61	**62**	**63**	**64**	**65**
5	1	7	0	2, 5
66	**67**	**68**	**69**	**70**
0	4, 5	0	3, 5	4
71	**72**	**73**	**74**	**75**
0	6	0	1	0
76	**77**	**78**	**79**	**80**
7	0	3, 7	0	2
81	**82**	**83**	**84**	**85**
5	0	1, 7	1, 4, 6	7

LETTERS MISSED

I. $\frac{}{1} \ \frac{}{2} \ \frac{}{3} \ \frac{}{4} \ \frac{}{5} \ \frac{}{6} \ \frac{}{7} \ \frac{}{8}$

II. $\frac{}{1} \ \frac{}{2} \ \frac{}{3} \ \frac{}{4} \ \frac{}{5} \ \frac{}{6} \ \frac{}{7} \ \frac{}{8}$

III. $\frac{}{1} \ \frac{}{2} \ \frac{}{3} \ \frac{}{4} \ \frac{}{5} \ \frac{}{6} \ \frac{}{7} \ \frac{}{8}$

IV. $\frac{}{1} \ \frac{}{2} \ \frac{}{3} \ \frac{}{4} \ \frac{}{5} \ \frac{}{6} \ \frac{}{7}$

V. $\frac{}{1} \ \frac{}{2} \ \frac{}{3} \ \frac{}{4} \ \frac{}{5} \ \frac{}{6} \ \frac{}{7} \ \frac{}{8}$

VI. $\frac{}{1} \ \frac{}{2} \ \frac{}{3} \ \frac{}{4} \ \frac{}{5} \ \frac{}{6} \ \frac{}{7}$

VII. $\frac{}{1} \ \frac{}{2} \ \frac{}{3} \ \frac{}{4} \ \frac{}{5} \ \frac{}{6} \ \frac{}{7} \ \frac{}{8}$

VIII. $\frac{}{1} \ \frac{}{2} \ \frac{}{3} \ \frac{}{4} \ \frac{}{5} \ \frac{}{6} \ \frac{}{7} \ \frac{}{8}$

IX. $\frac{}{1} \ \frac{}{2} \ \frac{}{3} \ \frac{}{4} \ \frac{}{5} \ \frac{}{6} \ \frac{}{7} \ \frac{}{8}$

X. $\frac{}{1} \ \frac{}{2} \ \frac{}{3} \ \frac{}{4} \ \frac{}{5} \ \frac{}{6} \ \frac{}{7} \ \frac{}{8}$

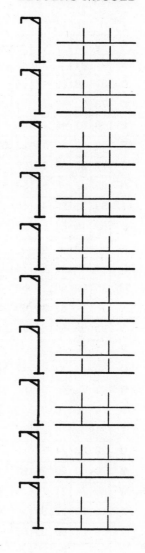

Par Score: 6

Your Score: _____

SOLITAIRE HANGMAN

LETTER CHART

	I	II	III	IV	V	VI	VII	VIII	IX	X
A	20	41	19	77	11	31	71	41	45	36
B	47	21	8	25	85	23	82	52	47	85
C	37	36	69	47	35	17	12	27	23	47
D	73	23	47	4	21	74	47	13	67	78
E	80	61	44	83	6	15	27	38	25	31
F	52	82	60	15	23	52	80	62	85	73
G	77	25	52	75	29	80	69	77	62	54
H	22	27	4	54	52	58	83	83	82	82
I	59	33	27	45	80	47	81	54	52	69
J	62	15	54	58	25	32	70	47	54	25
K	7	58	7	82	57	10	55	85	7	10
L	54	4	11	62	74	85	11	25	21	17
M	75	29	58	27	83	7	33	80	10	23
N	4	47	62	36	69	29	4	42	36	11
O	23	52	64	69	15	42	52	4	69	27
P	11	30	15	50	27	4	7	82	83	29
Q	58	54	73	70	47	54	58	69	70	21
R	43	73	40	21	54	62	54	15	17	70
S	74	80	70	37	58	69	15	7	73	4
T	21	2	16	23	7	83	62	11	58	33
U	29	83	74	73	42	21	25	73	74	72
V	70	69	29	29	62	77	21	21	27	52
W	83	74	21	74	70	66	29	58	77	74
X	15	70	77	80	4	70	73	70	4	58
Y	69	81	80	33	65	11	23	74	80	62
Z	25	62	83	52	33	73	74	23	11	77

| | I | II | III | IV | V | VI | VII | VIII | IX | X |

POSITION CHART

1	2	3	4	5
2, 3	1	2	0	7

6	7	8	9	10
5, 7	0	1	1, 7	4

11	12	13	14	15
0	3, 7	7	4	0

16	17	18	19	20
8	3	8	2	1, 6

21	22	23	24	25
0	5	0	3, 5, 8	0

26	27	28	29	30
1	0	8	0	3

31	32	33	34	35
6	5	0	6	3

36	37	38	39	40
7	4	3, 4	5	3

41	42	43	44	45
6	2	2, 8	4	2, 6

46	47	48	49	50
1	0	2	2, 6	1

51	52	53	54	55
8	0	2, 4	0	1, 4, 8

56	57	58	59	60
4	4	0	7	5

61	62	63	64	65
4, 8	0	5	6, 7	6

66	67	68	69	70
7	8	7	0	0

71	72	73	74	75
6	2	0	0	3

76	77	78	79	80
3	0	8	3	0

81	82	83	84	85
2	5	0	6	1

LETTERS MISSED

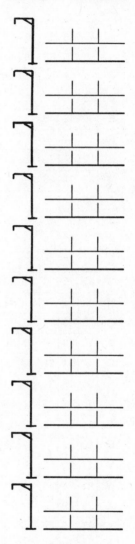

I. $\overline{}$
   1   2   3   4   5   6   7   8

II. $\overline{}$
    1   2   3   4   5   6   7   8

III. $\overline{}$
     1   2   3   4   5   6   7   8

IV. $\overline{}$
    1   2   3   4   5   6   7

V. $\overline{}$
   1   2   3   4   5   6   7

VI. $\overline{}$
    1   2   3   4   5   6   7

VII. $\overline{}$
     1   2   3   4   5   6   7   8

VIII. $\overline{}$
      1   2   3   4   5   6   7

IX. $\overline{}$
    1   2   3   4   5   6   7   8

X. $\overline{}$
   1   2   3   4   5   6   7   8

Par Score: 6

Your Score: _____

SOLITAIRE HANGMAN

LETTER CHART

	I	II	III	IV	V	VI	VII	VIII	IX	X
A	46	48	62	65	11	52	18	83	4	85
B	55	76	52	25	40	44	37	25	62	37
C	58	57	80	8	57	37	8	30	40	32
D	78	78	30	28	37	11	5	58	47	19
E	65	42	46	72	15	42	26	19	34	59
F	15	82	5	5	76	81	40	76	28	55
G	52	5	76	15	25	5	59	15	21	15
H	33	32	28	26	4	59	42	44	76	5
I	59	62	73	47	18	54	64	1	18	77
J	69	8	8	30	5	15	78	40	37	52
K	76	7	42	32	62	8	56	59	5	11
L	62	47	55	52	44	28	82	28	15	62
M	82	15	70	37	69	39	28	8	74	82
N	42	56	35	71	42	19	11	21	23	69
O	79	69	54	46	78	62	32	11	9	76
P	19	29	78	10	58	76	69	42	17	21
Q	5	11	21	19	82	21	44	74	82	78
R	66	19	37	55	43	65	45	23	30	50
S	8	4	65	82	65	25	17	82	25	40
T	54	55	59	45	8	30	65	62	60	4
U	10	37	19	40	19	56	15	26	78	25
V	11	21	11	59	52	32	47	32	8	83
W	21	25	15	42	21	40	10	69	32	65
X	28	28	25	62	28	55	25	37	42	66
Y	37	30	82	81	83	45	52	5	52	8
Z	25	40	32	11	30	82	55	78	44	28
	I	II	III	IV	V	VI	VII	VIII	IX	X

POSITION CHART

1	2	3	4	5
3,6,8	2,3	3	5	0
6	**7**	**8**	**9**	**10**
5	1,8	0	3	4
11	**12**	**13**	**14**	**15**
0	8	2	8	0
16	**17**	**18**	**19**	**20**
2	1	6	0	1,4,5
21	**22**	**23**	**24**	**25**
0	2	7	6	0
26	**27**	**28**	**29**	**30**
5	1	0	4	0
31	**32**	**33**	**34**	**35**
5	0	6	8	2,6
36	**37**	**38**	**39**	**40**
4	0	5	1,3,4	0
41	**42**	**43**	**44**	**45**
8	0	3,4	0	7
46	**47**	**48**	**49**	**50**
3	0	3,6	4	6
51	**52**	**53**	**54**	**55**
3,7,8	0	4	5	0
56	**57**	**58**	**59**	**60**
2	7	1	0	2
61	**62**	**63**	**64**	**65**
7	0	4,7	3	0
66	**67**	**68**	**69**	**70**
8	7	3	0	1,4
71	**72**	**73**	**74**	**75**
1	2,8	7	4	3
76	**77**	**78**	**79**	**80**
0	3,7	0	2,7	8
81	**82**	**83**	**84**	**85**
6	0	2	6	1,4

LETTERS MISSED

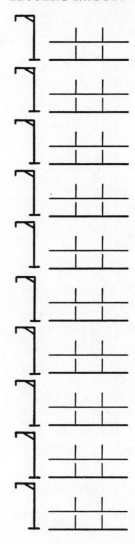

I. $\overline{}_1\ \overline{}_2\ \overline{}_3\ \overline{}_4\ \overline{}_5\ \overline{}_6\ \overline{}_7\ \overline{}_8$

II. $\overline{}_1\ \overline{}_2\ \overline{}_3\ \overline{}_4\ \overline{}_5\ \overline{}_6\ \overline{}_7\ \overline{}_8$

III. $\overline{}_1\ \overline{}_2\ \overline{}_3\ \overline{}_4\ \overline{}_5\ \overline{}_6\ \overline{}_7\ \overline{}_8$

IV. $\overline{}_1\ \overline{}_2\ \overline{}_3\ \overline{}_4\ \overline{}_5\ \overline{}_6\ \overline{}_7\ \overline{}_8$

V. $\overline{}_1\ \overline{}_2\ \overline{}_3\ \overline{}_4\ \overline{}_5\ \overline{}_6\ \overline{}_7$

VI. $\overline{}_1\ \overline{}_2\ \overline{}_3\ \overline{}_4\ \overline{}_5\ \overline{}_6\ \overline{}_7$

VII. $\overline{}_1\ \overline{}_2\ \overline{}_3\ \overline{}_4\ \overline{}_5\ \overline{}_6\ \overline{}_7$

VIII. $\overline{}_1\ \overline{}_2\ \overline{}_3\ \overline{}_4\ \overline{}_5\ \overline{}_6\ \overline{}_7\ \overline{}_8$

IX. $\overline{}_1\ \overline{}_2\ \overline{}_3\ \overline{}_4\ \overline{}_5\ \overline{}_6\ \overline{}_7\ \overline{}_8$

X. $\overline{}_1\ \overline{}_2\ \overline{}_3\ \overline{}_4\ \overline{}_5\ \overline{}_6\ \overline{}_7\ \overline{}_8$

Par Score: 4

Your Score: _____

SOLITAIRE HANGMAN

LETTER CHART

	I	II	III	IV	V	VI	VII	VIII	IX	X
A	34	56	79	81	35	83	39	30	43	73
B	24	28	8	68	43	43	41	82	24	58
C	73	15	73	85	2	26	46	51	45	9
D	26	2	80	15	8	63	68	63	65	23
E	15	79	4	45	49	56	80	2	85	3
F	8	35	23	80	10	75	63	75	48	35
G	53	20	75	35	45	60	26	45	28	26
H	62	76	57	50	48	73	53	1	35	75
I	43	13	78	56	33	8	35	23	14	16
J	75	43	43	53	50	78	43	50	75	8
K	20	8	48	8	53	24	2	10	83	53
L	35	48	35	78	72	45	78	15	79	78
M	23	50	45	48	56	18	33	20	50	45
N	68	23	56	82	69	10	56	8	68	83
O	18	74	84	21	80	35	72	56	56	63
P	45	68	50	10	5	20	45	27	23	32
Q	63	53	68	65	58	13	50	48	63	48
R	57	41	76	2	60	23	58	78	8	65
S	48	58	19	24	63	68	15	43	58	24
T	58	19	34	36	15	79	47	13	2	60
U	64	26	20	60	20	49	60	54	10	50
V	60	45	53	20	68	28	20	26	60	80
W	10	4	10	23	23	58	23	28	47	43
X	28	73	58	43	26	65	8	73	53	31
Y	50	63	60	73	65	15	48	65	69	82
Z	56	72	82	26	51	48	65	19	73	56

POSITION CHART

1	2	3	4	5
2, 8	0	5, 8	3	3, 4
6	**7**	**8**	**9**	**10**
6	1, 7	0	7	0
11	**12**	**13**	**14**	**15**
3	6	4	2	0
16	**17**	**18**	**19**	**20**
2	7	3	5	0
21	**22**	**23**	**24**	**25**
8	5	0	1	3,4
26	**27**	**28**	**29**	**30**
0	6	0	5	7
31	**32**	**33**	**34**	**35**
3	4	7	6, 8	0
36	**37**	**38**	**39**	**40**
2, 7	5	5	2, 4	4
41	**42**	**43**	**44**	**45**
8	8	2,6,8		0
46	**47**	**48**	**49**	**50**
1, 5	3	0	2, 5	0
51	**52**	**53**	**54**	**55**
1	5	0	3	1
56	**57**	**58**	**59**	**60**
0	2	0	2	0
61	**62**	**63**	**64**	**65**
1	5, 7	0	4	0
66	**67**	**68**	**69**	**70**
2	1	0	8	1, 2, 8
71	**72**	**73**	**74**	**75**
4	6	0	2	0
76	**77**	**78**	**79**	**80**
1	8	0	7	0
81	**82**	**83**	**84**	**85**
3, 6	0	6	4	4, 5

LETTERS MISSED

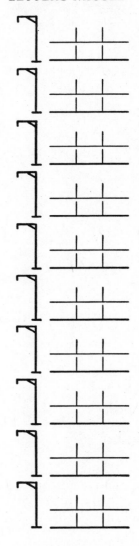

I. $\underline{\quad}\ \underline{\quad}\ \underline{\quad}\ \underline{\quad}\ \underline{\quad}\ \underline{\quad}\ \underline{\quad}\ \underline{\quad}$
    1   2   3   4   5   6   7   8

II. $\underline{\quad}\ \underline{\quad}\ \underline{\quad}\ \underline{\quad}\ \underline{\quad}\ \underline{\quad}\ \underline{\quad}\ \underline{\quad}$
    1   2   3   4   5   6   7   8

III. $\underline{\quad}\ \underline{\quad}\ \underline{\quad}\ \underline{\quad}\ \underline{\quad}\ \underline{\quad}\ \underline{\quad}\ \underline{\quad}$
    1   2   3   4   5   6   7   8

IV. $\underline{\quad}\ \underline{\quad}\ \underline{\quad}\ \underline{\quad}\ \underline{\quad}\ \underline{\quad}\ \underline{\quad}\ \underline{\quad}$
    1   2   3   4   5   6   7   8

V. $\underline{\quad}\ \underline{\quad}\ \underline{\quad}\ \underline{\quad}\ \underline{\quad}\ \underline{\quad}\ \underline{\quad}\ \underline{\quad}$
    1   2   3   4   5   6   7   8

VI. $\underline{\quad}\ \underline{\quad}\ \underline{\quad}\ \underline{\quad}\ \underline{\quad}\ \underline{\quad}\ \underline{\quad}$
    1   2   3   4   5   6   7

VII. $\underline{\quad}\ \underline{\quad}\ \underline{\quad}\ \underline{\quad}\ \underline{\quad}\ \underline{\quad}\ \underline{\quad}\ \underline{\quad}$
    1   2   3   4   5   6   7   8

VIII. $\underline{\quad}\ \underline{\quad}\ \underline{\quad}\ \underline{\quad}\ \underline{\quad}\ \underline{\quad}\ \underline{\quad}\ \underline{\quad}$
    1   2   3   4   5   6   7   8

IX. $\underline{\quad}\ \underline{\quad}\ \underline{\quad}\ \underline{\quad}\ \underline{\quad}\ \underline{\quad}\ \underline{\quad}\ \underline{\quad}$
    1   2   3   4   5   6   7   8

X. $\underline{\quad}\ \underline{\quad}\ \underline{\quad}\ \underline{\quad}\ \underline{\quad}\ \underline{\quad}\ \underline{\quad}\ \underline{\quad}$
    1   2   3   4   5   6   7   8

Par Score: 3

Your Score: _____

STAR ATTRACTIONS

REBUS CARTOONS

★★★☆

Puzzles by Henry Hook,
Emily Cox,
Henry Rathvon,
and Mike Shenk
Illustrations by Kimble Mead

How to Solve Rebus Cartoons

The picture puzzles known as cartoon rebuses have been popular diversions since the turn of the century, when *The Ladies' Home Journal* began a monthly page of them and gave cash prizes for their solutions. In the 1930s and again in the late 1950s, cartoon rebus contests swept the country as newspapers offered tens of thousands of dollars to readers who solved the difficult puzzles correctly.

GAMES revived these puzzles in 1981 for its sister publication, *The Four-Star Puzzler*, where they proved quite popular even without the lure of cash prizes. The best cartoon rebuses from *The Four-Star Puzzler* have been selected for this chapter.

How to Solve The answer to each cartoon rebus is the name of a person, place, or thing, and is found by combining any or all of the following elements:

- Words or hyphenated syllables spoken by the characters or found elsewhere in the picture;

- Synonyms of words spoken or appearing in the picture;

- Names of prominent objects in the picture;

- Isolated letters in the picture;

- Words implied by the action or subject of the scene.

These elements are combined phonetically to form a name fitting the category and the number of letters given as a clue for the cartoon.

Examples In the cartoon below left, the answer is Jimmy Connors. It is sounded out by the picture of the GYM, the word EEK spoken by the girl, and HONORS, a synonym for "award": GYM-EEK-HONORS. For the cartoon below right, the answer is *Vanity Fair*. It is solved by combining the VAN pictured in the background, the word IT spoken by the cabbie, the letter E on the van, and the word FARE, suggested by the scene: VAN-IT-E-FARE.

Answers to **Rebus Cartoons** start on page 373.

Tennis Player: 5, 7   **Magazine: 6, 4**

REBUS CARTOONS

1 Actor: 4, 6

2 Fictional Dog: 4

3 Inventor: 6, 6

4 Country: 4

5 Cartoon Character: 5

6 Animal: 7

7 U.S. River: 11

8 Crime: 7, 3, 7

9 Cartoon Character: 6

10 West Coast City: 5, 4

11 Tree: 8

12 Legendary Person: 4, 6

13 Comedian: 3, 4

14 Midwest City: 4, 5

15 Actress: 4, 5

16 TV Show: 4, 6

17 Food: 6, 8

18 Rock Musician: 5, 5

19 Book: 3–4

20 Composer: 4, 6

21 Nation: 5

22 French Author: 6

23 Wine: 8

24 Musical: 7

25 Sports Equipment: 8, 4

26 West Indian Nation: 5

27 Orchestra Conductor: 6, 9

28 Game: 5

29 Philosopher: 5

30 TV Character: 1, 1, 5

31 Swimmer: 4, 5

32 Baseball Player: 2, 4

REBUS CARTOONS

33 Singer/Actor: 4, 7

34 Far Eastern City: 6

35 Comic Strip Character: 5, 3

36 Historic Battle Site: 8

37 Pharaoh: 6

38 Great American Novel: 1, 8, 2, 4

39 Mythological Character: 8

40 Comedienne: 5, 7

41 University: 6

42 Movie Actor: 4, 6

43 Ancient City: 5, 6

44 Baseball Player: 3, 5

45 Cartoon Character: 4, 4

46 Midwest City: 9

47 TV Series: 4, 4

48 Indian Tribe: 6

49 Mythological Character: 4

50 European Capital: 8

51 Song: 3, 3, 3

52 TV Character: 6, 6

53 Broadway Musical: 6, 4

54 European City: 9

REBUS CARTOONS

55 World Leader: 6, 7

56 College: 8

57 Marathoner: 5, 7

58 Basketball Player: 6, 6

59 Show Song: 8

60 TV Actress: 4, 8

61 World Figure: 6, 2, 5

62 Baseball Player: 4, 5

63 TV Personality: 3, 10

64 Legendary Character: 9

65 Hockey Player: 4, 8

66 Baseball Team: 3, 5, 6

67 Constellation: 7

68 Actress: 6, 5

69 Classical Composer: 6

70 State Flower: 9

71 Motto: 2, 8

72 Popular Board Game: 7, 8

73 Broadway Musical: 2, 8

74 Rock Singer: 5, 8

75 Bandleader: 5, 6

76 Football Coach: 5, 6

77 Beatles Song: 3, 7

78 Country Singer: 7, 5

79 Drink: 7

80 Musical: 3–3

81 North African City: 7

82 Board Game: 9

83 Christmas Decoration: 9

84 Fashion Designer: 4, 6

85 Cartoonist: 1, 5

86 World Capital: 6

87 Wine: 3, 8

88 Cartoon Character: 6, 5

89 Fictional Character: 7, 4

90 TV Doctor: 6, 5

91 European Country: 7

92 Movie: 3, 4

REBUS CARTOONS

93 University: 6

94 Western Actor: 4, 5

95 South American Capital: 6

96 Outdoor Game: 7

97 Mideastern Region: 9

98 Comic Strip: 10

99 Actress: 3, 6

100 1960s Novel: 8, 9

101 Singer: 5, 4

102 Film Character: 6

103 Modern Artist: 9

104 Exclamation: 4, 3

105 Cartoon Character: 5, 3

106 Emperor: 10

107 Western: 8

108 World Leader: 8

109 Canadian City: 8

110 TV Personality: 4, 7

111 TV Show: 5, 7

112 Football Player: 1, 1, 6

113 TV Series: 1, 4, 4

114 Military Man: 6, 1, 3

115 Chess Player: 5, 7

116 Comedian: 4, 6

117 Storybook Character: 10

118 Newscaster: 6, 5

119 Mountain Range: 7

120 Jazzman: 5, 5

121 Children's Story: 5

122 American Author: 1, 1, 8

123 State: 7

124 Western Singer: 4, 8

125 Chemical Element: 8

126 Songwriting Team: 6, 3, 5

127 State: 12

128 Island Group: 4

129 Baseball Player: 7, 5

130 Cookbook Author: 6, 6

131 Tennis Player: 4, 7

132 Book and Movie: 3, 5, 6

133 Runner: 5, 9

134 Jazz Singer: 4, 5

135 Bay: 10

136 1920s Melody: 8, 2, 4

137 Pop Jazz Singer: 3, 5

138 Singer: 6, 7

139 Novel: 3, 4, 2, 3, 4

140 1970 Movie: 4, 4, 6

141 Comic Book and Movie: 8

142 Old TV Show: 2, 6, 3, 3

143 Midwestern City: 5

144 Song Oldie: 5, 7

145 Children's Author: 7, 6

146 Tourist Spot: 7

147   Pilot: 6, 7

148   PBS Series: 1, 8

149 Author: 6, 5, 5

150 Rock Star: 5, 11

THE
FOUR-STAR
PUZ?LER

by the Editors of GAMES

The Four-Star Puzzler

One of the hardest things in the world to do is to create an entirely new type of puzzle. The author of one puzzle book in 1944 said it couldn't be done—that all the good puzzle ideas in the world had been used up.

This chapter shows otherwise. It contains a grab bag of highly innovative puzzles based on words, mathematics, logic, trivia, observation, and mystery. All originally appeared in *The Four-Star Puzzler*, a 12-page (later a 16-page) monthly for expert puzzle solvers published by GAMES from 1981–83. The following problems are some of the editors' favorite brain-twisters from its pages. These novel challenges demonstrate that good puzzle ideas, like even the hardest solutions, can still be discovered.

Answers to **The Four-Star Puzzler** start on page 375.

1 Formality

LAUREL GEALT

Suppose all our songs were written in the manner we usually reserve for formal address. What they gained in dignity they might very well lose in understandability. Here are ten titles and lines from familiar songs, rendered quite formally; can you name all the originals?

1. I am overwhelmingly enthusiastic about President Truman.

2. Greetings, Ms. Madison; we are most pleased at your return to an accustomed niche.

3. Maintain equanimity, Ms. Bly, while the inclement weather dissipates.

4. Mr. Caine, please beach your skiff.

5. I am the owner of a sterile equine hybrid whom I address as Mr. Mineo.

6. An actual nepotal relative of my progenitor's sibling, Mr. Spade.

7. Into what realms have your recent travels taken you, young Mr. Martin?

8. Your countenance, Mr. Carson, almost failed to register with me.

9. Let us rendezvous, Mr. Armstrong, in a Mississippi River metropolis.

10. Do not exercise your lachrymal ducts on my account, Ms. York.

2 Paper Caper

MIKE SHENK

No loss, but our proofreader was kidnapped while working on this book. Shortly after, we received a ransom note composed of letters cut from newspaper headlines. (What lack of originality!) Unfortunately, the kidnapper was not careful enough to use good glue, because, when we opened the note, many of the cut-out letters were lying loose in the bottom of the envelope. By studying the loose pieces and the positions of the spots of glue left where missing pieces had been, we managed to restore the note to its original form, revealing the kidnapper's demands—which we, of course, refused to fulfill. But just what were those demands?

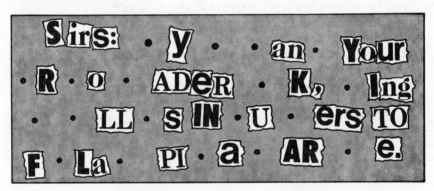

3 Can You Answer This? I

HENRY HOOK

1. Most TV fans know who J.R. Ewing is. But do you know what the initials J.R. stand for?

2. Speaking of names, the first three were Bob, David, and Frederic. The first three what?

3. "Lafayette, we are here!" What was Lafayette's response?

4. Why was it necessary for Admiral Byrd's Antarctic expedition to take along a refrigerator?

5. In 1491, James IV of Scotland demeaned it as "silly" and signed a law prohibiting it. Then one day he tried it, and soon the law was repealed. What is it?

6. Though mercury is classified as a liquid, it lacks one property common to most liquids. What property?

7. On December 6, 1926, it snowed in France. So what?

8. At an annual fiesta in Oaxaca, Mexico, local artists carve fantastic human and animal figures out of something quite unusual. What?

9. Another art question: Among Michelangelo's many masterpieces, why is his *Pieta* unique?

10. Newcomers to bullfights are led to believe that bulls can, but among mammals, only humans and monkeys can. Can what?

11. Trivia lovers know that Theodore Roosevelt was the first American President to ride in a car. But who was the first President to *drive* a car?

12. Who is or was Nikolai Tikhonov?

13. An unsuspecting hiker may suddenly find himself doused with a substance called ethanethiol. How might this happen?

14. Who held his position longer—President William Henry Harrison or Pope John Paul I?

15. What famous musical work was composed to celebrate the opening of the Suez Canal in 1871?

4 Missing Links I

GARY DISCH

The criss-cross grid below isn't quite finished. The 15 letters beneath it can be inserted to form a pattern of common words across and down. Can you find the unique solution?

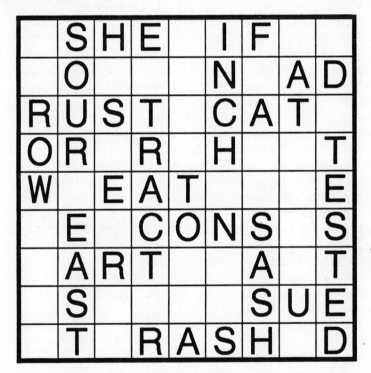

A A C C D E E F

H I O P R T X

5 Tollgate Trouble, Hardcase?
Three-Minute Detective

ROBERT L. LIDDIL

The North-South Tollway personnel disliked litter on their highway. Small wonder they were upset when, precisely at noon, all 280 pounds of Kurt "Jumbo" Schmaltz—punctuated by several .45-caliber exclamation points—was dumped beside the southbound lanes one mile north of the Bristol interchange by the occupants of a black limousine. Predictably, the toll personnel notified all toll booths to detain black limos, and summoned the police.

At 2:00 p.m. Inspector Hardcase and Jephro Homer were called to the Southpoint Tollgate (see map) to interrogate the occupants of three such vehicles being detained by a nervously perspiring attendant with a shotgun. She relaxed as Hardcase covered the suspects and Homer searched them for weapons.

She handed Hardcase the cars' toll tickets with their license numbers noted on the backs. Mr. and Mrs. Black's ticket showed they had entered at Northpoint at 11:55 a.m., "Dapper" Dan Savile and "Bullets" Blair had a ticket stamped "Concord—12:13 p.m.," and James Walker's read "Bristol—11:45 a.m."

Mrs. Black thrust her face belligerently into Hardcase's. "We demand that you release us immediately! We're in a hurry!"

Hardcase glanced at the time stamped on the Blacks' ticket and nodded. "Obviously."

Walker squirmed uncomfortably, then said, "I was having lunch about the time of the killing. These other guys can tell you—I was just starting dessert when they came into the Midway Diner and joined another man who was already there."

Hardcase glanced at the third ticket. "Car trouble, Bullets?"

"Yeah. Our coil wire broke and we had to splice it. You can check if you want to."

"Unnecessary," Hardcase answered. "I know who murdered Schmaltz."

Who?

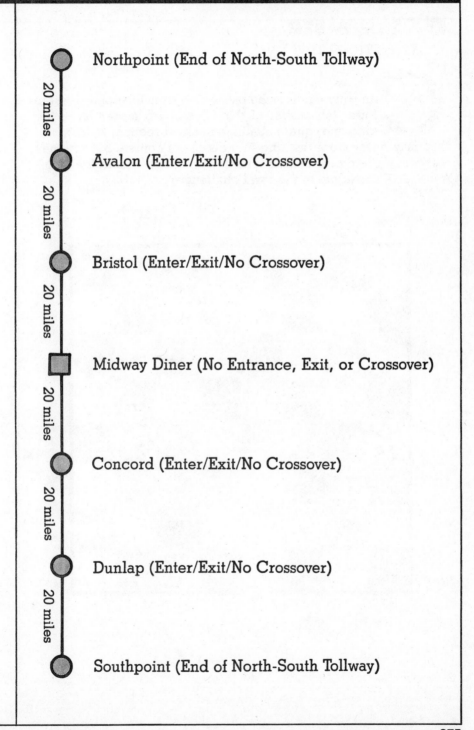

Northpoint (End of North-South Tollway)

20 miles

Avalon (Enter/Exit/No Crossover)

20 miles

Bristol (Enter/Exit/No Crossover)

20 miles

Midway Diner (No Entrance, Exit, or Crossover)

20 miles

Concord (Enter/Exit/No Crossover)

20 miles

Dunlap (Enter/Exit/No Crossover)

20 miles

Southpoint (End of North-South Tollway)

6 Chess Maze

KENNETH FEUCHT

Can you negotiate the black king from the upper right to lower left corner of this chessboard maze? Move the king one square at a time in any direction, as in chess. You may never move the king into check, of course, but you may capture white pieces (which remain stationary) to clear the king's path. Are you equal to the royal challenge?

Start ↘

↖ Finish

7 Skulduggery at the Flower Show
DENYS PARSONS

There were some shocking goings-on at this year's annual spring flower show at Fotherwingley, Worcestershire, England. The judge, Councillor Garfold, hatched a plot with his friend, Councillor Pertle. Pertle happened to say, "You know, some of these ladies would pay handsomely to win the first prize for flower arrangement."

"Well, what are we waiting for?" replied Councillor Garfold. "Go and find out who will pay the most. I'll give her the prize and we'll split the proceeds."

"OK, but we'll have to be careful." The two men agreed on a code signal, and Pertle went to sound out the competitors: Dame Diddrem, Mistress Lowdown, Ms. Pressed, Lady Hapramp, Mrs. Smootha, Madame Toadrod, and Miss Twister. Then he set up the agreed signal. He took seven spare vases and set one flower in each one; the initial letters of the flowers spelled the name of the highest bidder. But unluckily for the plotters, by the time of the prize-giving, some busybody had not only added other flowers to the seven vases but had changed the order of the vases on the shelf, with the following result:

First vase: anemone, erica, iris, ornithogalum, primula, ranunculus, wallflower.

Second vase: anemone, iris, lily, muscari, two ornithogalums, wallflower.

Third vase: hyacinth, lily, primula, scilla, two tulips, wallflower.

Fourth vase: three daffodils, ornithogalum, two scillas, tulip.

Fifth vase: anemone, iris, two ranunculi, scilla, two tulips.

Sixth vase: anemone, two daffodils, muscari, two narcissus, primula.

Seventh vase: three ericas, two hyacinths, muscari, wallflower.

Councillor Garfold was perplexed. But he could still have deduced which lady was willing to pay the highest bribe. Who was it?

8 Vacuum Packed

VIRGINIA C. McCARTHY

Arrange *all but one* of the numbers from 1 through 25 in the grid below so that each row's sum equals the number given at the left and each column's sum equals the number given at the top. The central row and central column are divided by heavy bars, and the sums given are for the squares *in front of* these bars; the sums for the remaining squares, to be deduced by the solver, should be entered in the central square.

Appearances to the contrary notwithstanding, the solution is unique!

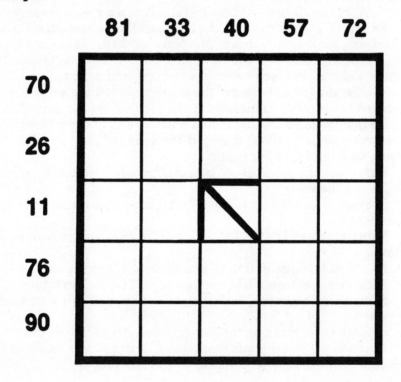

9 It's Your Turn

HENRY HOOK

1	2	3	4	5	6	7	8	9	10	11	12	13	14	15

Solve the 11 posers below and fill the answers in the squares above.

1. By reversing the name of one of the twelve months and removing one letter, you'll have a synonym for "pack." Write the removed letter, in lower case, in Square 15.

2. A synonym for "taxi" + a certain letter + a synonym for "mesh" = a seven-letter word. Write the "certain letter," in lower case, in Square 1.

3. A type of barrier has a homonym meaning "to condemn." Find the difference between the two words and write it, in lower case, in Square 13.

4. A certain five-letter word means both "a tally" and "a nobleman." Write its middle letter, in lower case, in Square 8.

5. The first and last (pen) names of *Alice in Wonderland*'s creator share one letter. As Alice might have seen that letter through the looking glass, write it in *upper* case in Square 11.

6. Alphabetically, what letter is as far from O as T is, but on the other side of O? Write it, in upper case, in Square 5, and put a hyphen through it.

7. Take a word for a kind of outdoor bed. Remove its first and last letters; the result reversed is a punctuation mark. Place this mark backwards in Square 12.

8. If $x^2 - x = -3$, find the two values for x and write their *product* in Square 10.

9. Subtract five from twice the cube of three. Write the positive square root of the result in Square 2.

10. Two of the six remaining squares have numbers that are upside-down images of one another. *Draw* "an anagram of CLERIC" in each of the other four squares.

11. If you've solved all ten of the above posers, turn the page upside-down and read the message in the squares.

🔟 Worthy of Note
A Cross-Letter Puzzle

VIRGINIA C. McCARTHY

Use the clues to arrange the 21 listed letters in the diagram. When you are done, you can find the names of eight composers by reading consecutive adjacent letters—which may progress in any direction, including diagonally. The letters in the shaded squares, when rearranged, spell a relevant musical instrument. (Note: In the clues, the letter Y is not referred to as either a vowel or a consonant.)

A A B C D E H I L M N

O O P R S T U V Y Z

ACROSS

1. The second letter is alphabetically preceded by all the other letters in 2-Down.

3. Two letters are vowels.

5. All letters are consonants.

6. A vowel followed by the letters in LACE scrambled.

7. Contains all but one of the letters in PEND.

DOWN

1. Two consecutive vowels followed by three musical notes other than E.

2. Contains all but one of the letters in CRAZY.

3. The last four letters are the letters in CHIN scrambled.

4. All letters are consonants; and the second letter is alphabetically preceded by all other letters in its column and row.

5. The first letter comes alphabetically *before* the first letter in 4-Down and *after* the first letter in 3-Down.

THE FOUR-STAR PUZZLER

11 Flights of Fancy

KATHLEEN MELLON

On a fine, sunny day with a touch of magic, five true friends (Brigett, Eomann, Maire, Padraig, and Sean) headed off to a picnic in a secluded area. After eating, each went off alone to enjoy the natural beauty of the woods. Each had a vision of a mythological creature (a dragon, a griffin, a leprechaun, a pixie, a unicorn) in a part of the forest (in a cave, in a dell, on a hilltop, in a meadow, behind a tree). One thought it was a dream, another an hallucination; but the other three gave immediate chase. One of the five actually caught a glimpse of a real creature. Which one?

CLUES

1. The griffin was not seen by Padraig and was not chased by anyone.

2. The creature on the hilltop was chased by a boy but was not real.

3. Brigett did not see the griffin but did see a creature in the dell.

4. The pixie was not seen in the cave, on the hilltop, or behind a tree and was not chased.

5. The dragon was chased but the creature in the cave was not.

6. A boy saw the unicorn but not on the hilltop and not behind a tree.

7. One of the girls saw the leprechaun but it was not real.

8. Neither Sean nor his friend Maire saw a creature in the meadow but both gave chase.

9. The real creature was seen in neither cave nor dell, but it was chased.

10. Neither Padraig nor Eomann thought he was hallucinating and neither saw a creature on the hilltop.

12 A Little Deduction

HENRY HOOK

Find the five-letter words that answer the eight clues below. You'll know if you have chosen the right words because a message will be formed by taking the one letter from each word that appears in no other word among the eight.

1. Austrian composer Joseph _____   _ _ _ _ _
2. Goodyear's emblem   _ _ _ _ _
3. Pirate's eyepiece   _ _ _ _ _
4. Reeks, as auto exhausts   _ _ _ _ _
5. Granny's wrap   _ _ _ _ _
6. Bryant Gumbel's show   _ _ _ _ _
7. Painter's need   _ _ _ _ _
8. Like good piecrust   _ _ _ _ _

13 On a First-Name Basis

DOUG and JANIS HELLER

Each group of first names below belongs to four famous personalities (real or fictional) with something in common. You needn't give all four last names; just find the something-in-common. For example, the names Eli, Thomas, Robert, and Alexander all belong to inventors (Whitney, Edison, Fulton, Graham Bell).

1. Johnny, Hank, Kenny, Dolly
2. George, Hubert, Barry, Adlai
3. Jane, Debby, Lucie, Shaun
4. Arthur, John, Jimmy, Virginia
5. Alfred, Mel, Otto, Roman
6. Charles, Walt, Garry, Chic
7. Alan, Loretta, Jamie, Mike
8. Alan, John, Frank, Neil
9. Bob, Bill, Gene, Richard
10. Conrad, Eddie, Richard, John
11. Jane, Sam, Nick, Charlie
12. Margaret, Ray, Bert, Frank
13. Roger, Terry, Joe, Fran
14. Phyllis, Mary Ann, Lee, Bess
15. Susan, Julie, Margaret, Patti
16. Les, Betty, Karen, Pete
17. Janet, Peggy, Linda, Dorothy
18. Bobby, Larry, José, Boris
19. Ben, Lou, Perry, Barney
20. Andrew, Michael, Kate, Jesse

14 Aunt Hildegarde I

DAVID DIEFENDORF

My Aunt Hildegarde is a dear old bird, but a slightly daffy one. How can I explain her likes and dislikes when they change every month? Last month, for example, she liked bees but not honey, eggs but not toast, shooting pool but not playing badminton—and all because her fancy had been caught by the *double letters* of words. (So last month she liked *letters* but not *words*!) Anyway, she's on a new kick this month. Can you figure out what principle is guiding her giddy tastes?

This month Aunt Hildegarde is striving for NOTORIETY, not for FAME.

She's walking around on STILTS, but she won't go near her ROLLER SKATES.

She wants to buy some pet TURTLES, but she doesn't fancy FROGS.

She likes KLEENEX but not TOILET PAPER.

She laughs at ABBOTT but not at COSTELLO.

She's wearing OPALS but not DIAMONDS.

She's reading GHOST stories but not VAMPIRE tales.

She prefers NORMANS to SAXONS.

She applauds EFFORT and avoids DRUDGERY.

She's crazy about DESSERTS but doesn't care for APPETIZERS.

15 Tic-Tac-Total?

IRVIN ROY HENTZEL
and RONALD K. SMITH

The two tots Tillie and Willie were playing tic-tac-toe one rainy afternoon, but they grew tired of all the tie games they were having. After some thought, they hit on a new way to play. Instead of X's and O's, one player used the numbers 1,3,5,7,9 and the other used the numbers 2,4,6,8. The ODD player, having an extra move, was to go first. Players then alternated playing their numbers on the tic-tac-toe grid, one digit per square; no number could be played more than once. The player who placed his or her number so that the sum of three numbers in a line (horizontally, vertically, or diagonally) totaled 15 was the winner. If at the end of a game no player had achieved a line totaling 15, the game was declared a tie—but Tillie and Willie found that, for one rainy afternoon at least, they were playing a game in which they could outsmart each other.

Positions from two of their games are shown below as puzzles, the first rather easier than the second.

1. Find a move for EVEN that will result in a win.

2. Find a move for ODD that will result in a win.

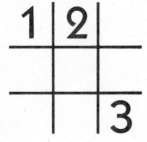

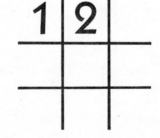

16 Crystal Clear

PIERRE BERLOQUIN

No pencil or paper on this one. Imagine that each of the four 6×6 diagrams below is printed on a sheet of transparent glass. If each diagram is rotated 90° in the direction shown, and then all four are stacked (in any order) on top of one another, how many of the 36 small squares would *not* be blacked out?

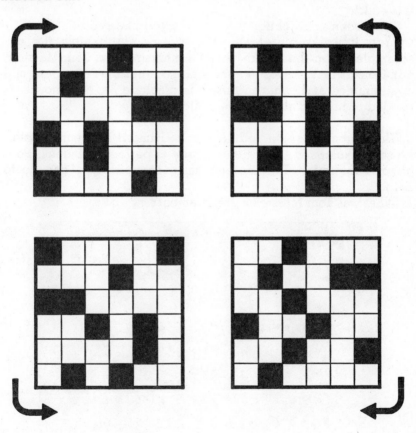

17 Consul in Trouble
DENYS PARSONS

Sir Percy Wipplegrave, the new British Ambassador in Moscow, was being shown the ropes by his subordinates. In the cable room he was told, "Of course all the cables to and from London are in code, but for our Consulates in the USSR we find it sufficient to use a scrambler. The messages are merely anagrammed, transmitted, and then unscrambled at this end."

"That seems straightforward," said the Ambassador.

"Yes, it works quite well, but today unfortunately the unscrambler is on the blink. Here's a message from Tom Marston, our Consul in Vladivostok. You can see that the letters are still anagrammed and, what's worse, the machine has somehow succeeded in turning all the vowels into Z's."

The Ambassador studied the cable. Himself no mean puzzler, he soon exclaimed, "But the message is perfectly obvious. Poor chap! Poor chap! For heaven's sake, see what you can do to help him."

What was Tom Marston's predicament?

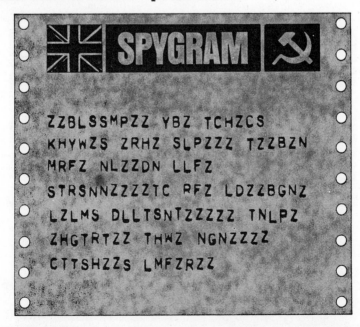

SPYGRAM

```
ZZBLSSMPZZ YBZ TCHZCS
KHYWZS ZRHZ SLPZZZ TZZBZN
MRFZ NLZZDN LLFZ
STRSNNZZZZTC RFZ LDZZBGNZ
LZLMS DLLTSNTZZZZZ TNLPZ
ZHGTRTZZ THWZ NGNZZZZ
CTTSHZZS LMFZRZZ
```

18 In a Word

DOUG and JANIS HELLER

Each group of words and phrases below disguises a well-known set of items. Each word or phrase contains, reading from left to right in proper order—but interspersed with extraneous letters—a smaller word. In every group, these smaller words comprise a complete set.

1. Trombone
   Dill pickle
   Heart-weary

2. Disharmonized
   Calculable
   Three-quarter
   Desperadoes

3. Mismatching paints
   Contrarious
   Housebroken
   Oversize
   Supervisor

4. Joshing
   Peaceful
   Page-for-page
   Farmington

19 In Summation
NOLA OBEE

In this puzzle, 1 + 1 is never 2. In each equation, take the word for the first number and add to it—in front, behind, or on both sides—the number of letters indicated to form the answer defined. For example, "1 + 1 = zero" would have for its answer NONE (the word ONE with one other letter added).

a. 9 + 5 = balcony

b. 8 + 3 = increase

c. 1 + 2 = gas

d. 1 + 4 = weapon

e. 2 + 6 = letter carrier

f. 10 + 5 = metal

g. 1 + 5 = bird trainer

h. 9 + 4 = madcap quality

i. 1 + 4 = big cat

j. 10 + 3 = little cat

k. 2 + 5 = tree

l. 4 + 3 = mathematician

20 Who Plays What?
Logic Problem

LEIGH KING

Five members of the Piggin String Symphony Orchestra got together for coffee after rehearsal. Each one bore a name that identified an instrument played by one of their number. Only one of the group played the instrument indicated by his/her own name. Conversation naturally turned to the music they had been practicing. Each player had a favorite among the four selections; these compositions were Bach's *Toccata and Fugue in G Minor*, Mozart's *Concerto for Flute and Harp*, Brahms' *First Symphony*, and Stravinsky's *The Rite of Spring*. (Two of the five agree.)

From the clues below, determine the full name, instrument, and favorite composition of each person. (Note: Solution requires knowledge of when each composer wrote.)

CLUES

1. The group was hardly seated when Ms. Harper and the violinist excused themselves to the powder room. Joseph rose courteously at their exit.

2. Robert commented that no good music had been written since 1800, and all wind instruments should be barred from orchestral membership.

3. Richard replied, "Regardless, I think Angela and I blend well as soloists and, for this concert at least, Mozart is our favorite composer."

4. Pfeiffer turned to the violinist and commented that his taste favored twentieth-century music. At about this time the ladies returned to the table.

5. One of the group remarked, "I wish the conductor wouldn't call me simply by my last name; 'Harris' sounds so impersonal."

6. Horner, speaking to Fiddler, mentioned his admiration for string music and expressed his desire to learn to play the viola.

21 Mix and Match

MIKE SHENK

This puzzle is two puzzles in one. First, rearrange the letters of each of the 10 words in the numbered list and each of the 10 words in the box below it to create a set of 20 anagrams. Then match each of the anagrams in the list to one from the box to form a common two-word phrase. Beware of words that have more than one anagram. An example has been provided to get you started.

Ex. ARCHES   *search*   *parties*
1. BECHARM
2. ENLARGE
3. FOREST
4. GROAN
5. LONGED
6. MARITAL
7. PLAYER
8. RINGLETS
9. STREAM
10. UNCLEAR

ARTICLE	CARTHORSE	ESTRANGE
CREATION	ENTRAP	LURE
GEARMAN	LIVERS	STAR
~~PIRATES~~	STAGE	

22 Chess Search

MIKE SHENK

This is really two puzzles in one—a word search puzzle and a chess problem. To start, find the names of 12 chess pieces hidden on the chessboard in horizontal, vertical, or diagonal lines. Instead of circling the whole words, however, circle only the first letter of each—except for any knights you may find, for which you should circle the Ns to distinguish them from the kings. When you're done, the 12 circled letters will give the board positions of the pieces in the chess problem. All men on ranks 1–4 are white, and all on ranks 5–8 are black. Then it's White's move and mate in four.

8	W	N	I	K	R	O	O	K
7	A	N	E	E	U	Q	I	P
6	P	O	B	I	S	N	O	A
5	O	K	N	I	G	H	T	W
4	H	O	N	W	S	O	R	N
3	S	O	R	I	A	H	O	A
2	I	R	B	N	G	P	O	W
1	B	T	H	G	N	I	K	P

23 Uncle Jack, the Hero?

DENYS PARSONS

The young twins Roger and Peter were on a visit to their great-uncle Jack in Toronto.

"Did I ever tell you boys about the British scientific expedition to west Greenland in 1930?" Uncle Jack did not wait for an answer. "Well, the three-man team was in a very isolated spot, and when no radio contact had been made for a long time, the British authorities became worried. The Canadian government knew of my Arctic experience and offered to send me out to try to trace them. It was a hair-raising journey in a tiny seaplane fitted with floats instead of wheels, and our altimeter and hydrometer were not working properly. The pilot dropped me at the coast and for four days I trudged inland alone through thick snow.

"Eventually I reached the expedition's cabin. The thermometer just inside the door registered five degrees below zero Fahrenheit! There were the members of the team, huddled at the table almost as if in conversation, but stone dead—frozen to death, I surmised. The cabin contained almost no food, and I could have done with a change after my daily diet of penguin meat. Curiously enough, there was a plentiful supply of beer, and I lost no time in downing a couple of cans. The cabin was stacked with mineral specimens, animal skins, and cans of film which the team had been preparing for a TV science series, but these were too heavy for me to carry back. I buried the four men in a shallow snow grave and took back only their farewell messages to their families in Britain.

"The journey back to the plane was exhausting and I had to shoot a fox for food to keep me alive. Although I brought back bad news, when we hit the airstrip at Fredericton, New Brunswick, I had a terrific reception from the press and public, and there were congratulatory telegrams from the Queen of England and from President Hoover."

"That's a great story, Uncle Jack," said Roger. "What a pity we can't believe a word of it."

Why couldn't the boys believe Uncle Jack's tale of heroism?

24 Syllasteps

WILL SHORTZ

The two diagonal flights of stairsteps will spell related words when you are finished. To discover them, use the word fragments in the Syllabary to form eight four-syllable words that answer the clues given. Cross off the syllables as you use them, because each is used once and only once. Enter the answers across the grid, one syllable per space—then see what the shaded spaces spell reading from upper left to lower right.

Syllabary

AC AL AR ATE BI CAM CIL COL DE ER ER
FLAGED FRIG GY IS LA LEG LO MAIN O OL OS
OU PUNC QUI RE TION TLE TO TURE U UN

Clues

1. One of the sciences
2. Not hidden
3. Keep cool
4. Slangy
5. Sleight of hand
6. Greek philosopher
7. Instability
8. Form of medicine

25 Escape From the Labyrinth

DENYS PARSONS

Hi, Theseus! Going into the labyrinth? Take this clay tablet—the inscription tells you how to get out again."

"See here, Ariadne, you know perfectly well you're supposed to provide me with a ball of thread."

"Ball of thread? What a quaint idea. My tablet is much more scientific. You see, the labyrinth is rectangular and laid out in unit squares. The tablet shows that the only way from the center is to go one square north, one square east, and one square south—and all through the labyrinth it gives you a compass direction for the next move. The final sign brings you to the door through which a further step in the same direction delivers you into the open air. And in case you should make a mistake, I've indicated the four blind alleys on this smaller tablet, so that every square of the maze is covered. Good luck now... Oh Thesie, you idiot!"

Alas, Theseus had dropped the larger tablet onto the rocks and it had shattered into six pieces.

"By Zeus, Ariadne, I'm really in for it now. The Minotaur is sure to get me!"

Can you save Theseus by drawing the complete maze? Here are the fragments, in no particular order after the first, where C stands for center:

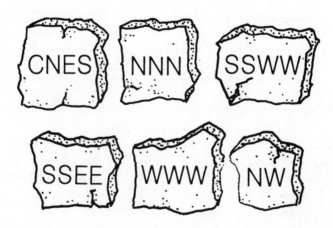

And here are the blind alleys in the order they are met with when walking from the center to the exit:

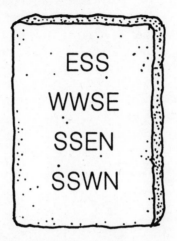

ESS
WWSE
SSEN
SSWN

Finally, here's a piece of squared paper (more than you'll need) that may help you in straightening out the paths of the maze:

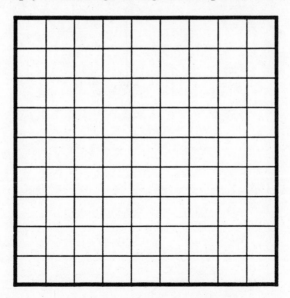

26 Cube Words

WILL SHORTZ

How many five-letter words can you find in the block of letters below? A word may start at any letter, but must proceed along balls that are consecutively connected by straight lines. For example, the word UPSET starts at the U in the middle of the cube's front side, moves down to the P, backwards to the S, up to the E, and then left to the T. In forming a word you may return to a letter and use it again (as in TACIT), but you may not stand on a letter and use it twice before proceeding (as in ATTIC). Disallowing capitalized and hyphenated words, but allowing plurals, we found 31 common five-letter words in the block. We invite you to top our score.

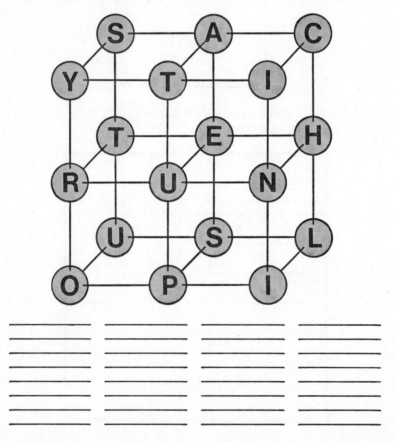

27 The N+t+ce B++rd

DENYS PARSONS

Some of the most beautiful British gardens are those of the so-called "stately homes." This year I took my family to Lord Brankshead's estate in Derbyshire. As we entered the drive we saw a notice displayed for the attention of the public. It was a sorry sight, as a non-weatherproof adhesive had been used to stick the plastic letters on the board, and three-quarters of them had fallen to the ground.

```
+H++  +++D++  ++  +++N
F++   +++   ++NE+++   ++
+++   ++B+++.
+L++++   +EE+   ++   +++
+++TP++++  ++D  ++  +OT
++CK   ++Y   +++W+++.
         ++++   ++++++
         ES++TE  MA++GE+
```

Who was the anonymous Estate Manager, I idly wondered, and while the rest of the family looked 'round the garden, I made a note of the fallen letters:

AAAAAAAABCDDDEEEEEEEEEEEFFFFGHHHHIIIIIKLL
MNNNNNOOOOOOOOOPPPPRRRRRRSSSSSSTTTTTTT
TU

What was the Estate Manager's fitting name?

28 Aunt Hildegarde II

DAVID DIEFENDORF

The last time I saw Aunt Hildegarde, she liked pies but not brownies, church but not Sunday school, bed but not board. The reason, she explained, was that she liked words whose first and last letters were separated by the same number of letters as in the alphabet. (PieS/PqrS, etc.). That's why she'd given away her octopus for a new pet *rat* (RsT). But Aunt Hildegarde has been spending time with Aunt Mame recently, and it seems to have affected her likes and dislikes. Can you tell what principle is guiding her tastes this month?

This month Aunt Hildegarde likes to use PAPRIKA, not CURRY.

She likes an OCTAGON, not a SQUARE.

She'd rather be GOING than COMING.

She prefers LITTLE to BIG.

Yet she loves her pet RHINOCEROS, and has given away her RAT.

She drives a VOLVO, never a DATSUN.

She likes a HEATH, not a MOOR.

She'll attend a BARBECUE, but does not like a ROAST.

She can deal with OBLIGATIONS, but can't meet COMMITMENTS.

She likes BASEBALL, hates FOOTBALL.

She goes in and out the WINDOW, never uses a DOOR.

29 Matching Wits

MORGAN WORTHY

Items in the two columns below can be matched up. In each matching pair, one of the items has been disguised by some form of wordplay or double meaning; the disguised item may be on the left or on the right. No special knowledge is required—just a flexible mind and a sense of the ridiculous. To give you just a flavor of this sort of puzzle, I can say that you should be prepared to match "Manifold" with "Codger" (man if old) and "Hum animated" with "My spouse" (human I mated).

_____	**1.** To players	**A.**	Legends about Devil
_____	**2.** Missing South	**B.**	Of flight
_____	**3.** Latin	**C.**	Star theirs
_____	**4.** Pardoned	**D.**	Pitch pipe
_____	**5.** Double cross	**E.**	Giant
_____	**6.** Swamp	**F.**	Best in the barnyard
_____	**7.** Keystone	**G.**	Scan them
_____	**8.** Back issues	**H.**	Dirtied by birds
_____	**9.** Implore	**I.**	Wetter rain
_____	**10.** Bug a soldier	**J.**	His panic
_____	**11.** State hymn	**K.**	Same side of street
_____	**12.** Crowding yawning	**L.**	Newest

30 Proverbs

DENYS PARSONS

Our Scottish friend Jock McCann is obsessed with proverbs. He constantly uses them in his conversation. So one day we decided to set him a little proverb puzzle.

"Here you are, Jock," we said. "Take this list of words and fit them into the frame, one word per box, to make proverbs reading across and down. Each one should take you only a moment."

"Ay, but *many a mickle mak's a muckle*, as we say in Scotland. Or, as you would say, it soon adds up."

"Yes, we included that proverb in your honor. But there are twelve other well-known proverbs in our puzzle, and four of them are red herrings—that is, they *don't* fit in the frame."

"Well, here's a proverb for you. *When a herring is red, you'll feel better in bed.* How's that?"

"Lousy," we replied. "Now Jock, just fill in the frame. Here's your list of words. There's one word for each box, and of course there are all the words for the four red herring proverbs, too. When you've finished the frame, you can tell me what those four are."

A A A A A A A A AN AND AND AND APPLE ARE AWAY BROTH CAT'S CHILD CLOUD COOKS DAY DOCTOR EVERY FOOL FOR GATHERS HANDS HAS HAS HIS IN IT'S KEEPS LIGHT LINING ROAD LONG MAKE MAK'S MAN MANY MANY MICE MICKLE MONEY MOSS MUCKLE NINE NO NO PARTED PLAY ROD ROLLING SAVES SILVER SOON SPARE SPOIL STITCH STONE THAT THE THE THE THE THE THE THERE'S THERE'S TIDE TIME TOO TURNING WAIT WAY WHEN WHERE WILL WORK

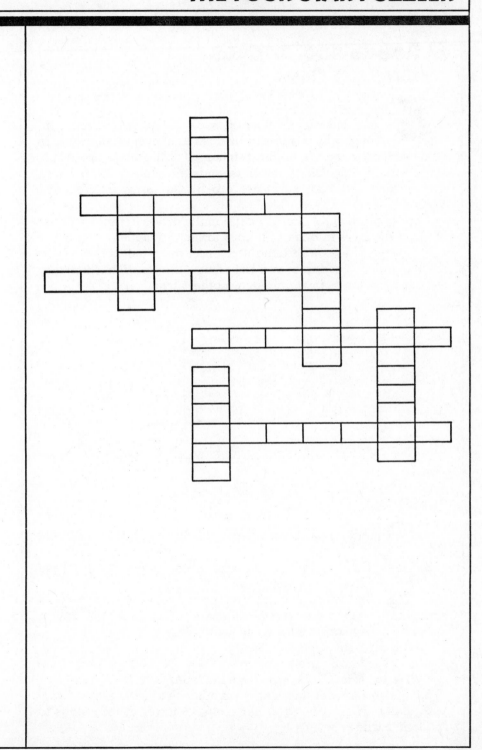

31 Roads and Bridges
NECAH BÜYÜKDURA

A married couple lives in each of the four towns connected by roads and bridges as shown on the map. In alphabetical order, the names of the wives are Anne, Betty, Claire, and Diana; the husbands are Henry, John, Larry, and Orson; and their surnames are Black, Gray, Scarlet, and White.

Each of these eight people occasionally drives to visit his or her mother who lives in one of the four towns; no mother lives in the same town as her son or daughter. From the clues below, match these people's first names and last names, the towns in which they live, and the towns in which their mothers live.

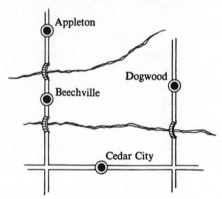

CLUES
1. Two mothers live in each town.

2. Two mothers of the same couple do not live in the same town.

3. Betty Scarlet and Anne, who lives in Beechville, have mothers who live in the same town.

4. The numbers of bridges crossed by some of these people when they travel to see their mothers are:

    a. 3 for Orson, whose name is not Gray;

    b. 3 for Betty;

    c. 2 for Mr. Scarlet;

    d. 2 for Mrs. Black, who lives in Cedar City.

5. Claire's mother and Henry's mother live in the same town.

6. Betty, when driving to her mother's town, usually stops to see John's wife.

32 Soccer Match

B. UPTON-ROWLEY

Great Britain, Ireland, Russia, and Spain are playing one another in soccer. A number of games have been completed, and a reporter is arranging his notes for a newspaper story. Unfortunately, a computer error has left his chart, below, incomplete. By examining the chart and the clues accompanying it, however, you should be able to name the winner, the loser, and the score of every game that has been played. (Note: in the chart, a win results in 2 points for the victor; a tie results in 1 point per team.)

CLUES

1. There has not been a game for every possible match-up of teams, and no team has played the same opponent more than once.

2. One team won a game by 5–1. No other team scored as many as 5 goals in any game.

3. One team won one of its games by 1 goal more than it won another game.

Teams	Games Played	Games Won	Games Lost	Games Tied	Total Goals For	Ag.	Points
G.B.		2				0	
Ire.	2				2		2
Rus.				0			
Sp.	3					11	1

33 The Singer and the Song

J.F. PEIRCE

Robert Bowles, dubbed the "Bagel Bandit" by the press, was apprehended near the scene of a jewelry-store heist when he dropped a sack of bagels and some stolen loot.

Confronted with a possible life sentence as a habitual criminal, Bowles offered to "sing" against the other members of his gang in return for a promise of immunity from prosecution. Since his testimony would clear up twenty robberies and put the rest of the gang in prison, the district attorney agreed.

At the trial, the bailiff handed Bowles a note. Bowles read the note slowly, then wadded it into a ball and threw it on the floor. When he was sworn in a short time later, he pleaded the Fifth Amendment and refused to testify, even though the D.A. threatened to "throw the book" at him.

The judge dismissed the case, and the D.A. watched angrily as the defendants went free and the bailiff led Bowles from the courtroom. As he was on the point of leaving, the D.A. remembered the note Bowles had thrown on the floor, and he remembered how Bowles had turned white while reading it. Going back to the table, he picked it up.

He frowned once he'd straightened the note out. On it was drawn a musical staff with musical notation, as follows:

Obviously the note was a code, probably one sent by the defendants. The D.A. sat down at the table and studied the note carefully. After several minutes he succeeded in deciphering the message, and he understood why Bowles had refused to testify.

What did the message say?

34 Keeping In Step

MERL REAGLE

The diagram below can be filled with words progressing from one letter in length to eleven letters. Each new word is a rearrangement of the word preceding it, with one more letter added at each step (e.g., A, AT, TAR, ARTS, SITAR, etc.). Clues for the eleven words are listed *in mixed order*. See if you can find all eleven words and match them with their clues.

a. Answering one melody with another?
b. "____ Reply" (Beatles song)
c. Start of a carol
d. Member of a Roman band
e. Barber shop quartet singer
f. Opening number
g. Give a sound beating
h. Piano work
i. Lacking harmony
j. Crotchet or quaver
k. Trumpet's relative

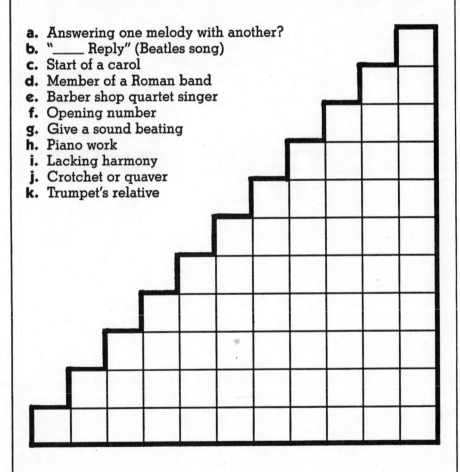

35 The Game Devisers

VIRGINIA C. McCARTHY

One drab day when Perce and Eve were reduced to thumb-twiddling, Perce suddenly brightened and said, "I'll think of a positive number of 75 or less. Ask me yes-or-no questions and see how quickly you can guess the number." Eve, who had never been known to ask an irrelevant question, plunged in thusly:

1. Is it a prime number?
2. Is it divisible by 2?
3. Is it divisible by 3?
4. Is it divisible by 5?
5. Is it less than 25?

The questions are given in the order Eve asked them. After the fifth question was answered—and not before—Eve had ferreted out Perce's number. Can you find the number and the answers Perce gave to the five questions?

36 Break Time

HENRY HOOK

Someone took a hammer to the clock shown here and smashed it to bits. Maybe the clock struck first? Anyway, see if you can reconstruct the clock face and tell us what time it said when it was broken. Using just your eyes, please.

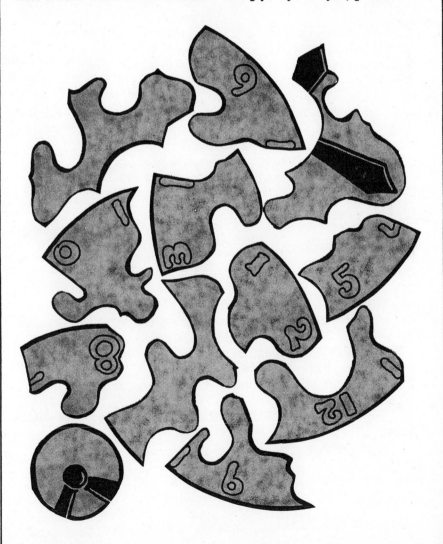

▣ Can You Answer This? II

HENRY HOOK

Here are some more questions to test your knowledge of the extraordinary, the arcane, and the just plain trivial.

1. "What a dream it was—what a nightmare it has become," said what famous inventor, and under what circumstances?

2. What should you feed your grown-up pet moth?

3. Is a man or a woman more likely to stutter?

4. When the Spanish Armada invaded England, how many British ships were sunk, within 50?

5. It first appeared in 1892 in *Youth's Companion*, a boys' magazine, as part of a Columbus Day promotion. What is it?

6. By what name is Anna Kemenes better known?

7. What is the only native American breed of dog?

8. Twice daily, a panel of five men gets together in a small office in London to determine an important international statistic. Which?

9. Oddly, all three of the following blanks will take the same number: For every ___ individual children born, one set of twins is born; for every ___ sets of twins born, one set of triplets is born; and for every ___ sets of triplets, one set of quadruplets.

10. And along the same lines, what is the commonest, and often the only, difference between a set of identical twins?

11. About 1/6 of all Tibetan men follow the same occupation. What is it?

12. Charles Dickens once called them "nearly always the obstructors of society." Who are they?

13. Whatever happened to the first typewritten manuscript for publication?

14. How many cups of coffee did William Shakespeare drink per day?

38 This, That, and the Other

LYNN MARIE HYDE

Each of the names below is a rearrangement of the letters of a familiar phrase known to every Tom, Dick, and Harry. The professions of these fabricated persons have been given as hints to help you sort the phrases out.

1. ANNA P. DAPPERCLOCKS—cereal saleswoman

2. HUBERT DEAN WILDE—flagman

3. LADY DIANA BELLWINGER—volunteer worker

4. DONALD "SKAT" HALDERMAN—male model

5. SONIA DINKLEHONKER—fishwife

6. DONNA LEE BALDBLOCK—witch

7. CARLA T. BOLDKNOCKERS—popgun maker

8. GENE "SIDE-SADDLE" DAREDEVLIN—Pony Express rider

39 Missing Birds

ROBERT GRAY

My stenographer has a phobia: She will not type the names of birds! Her watchful eye saw the word HAWK in the following sentence: "Because of the t*haw k*een ice skaters were disappointed." She deleted the word, altered the spacing, and produced: "Because of the tee nice skaters were disappointed."

Below are ten more samples of my stenographer's work. In every case, one bird has been deleted, and liberties have been taken with the spacing. The number of letters in each bird's name is given in parentheses. Can you restore the original sentences?

1. Sebastian Coe finished strongly after two slaps. (3)
2. The cook complained about working with the ban. (4)
3. He was fascinated by the conjurer and hid. (4)
4. The tenant was perfectly happy to pay the lot. (4)
5. We marched to music provided by the drummers of a Scottish regiment. (9)
6. As you have lost my letter, here is a note. (5)
7. The farmer was used to sowing in the mud. (7)
8. "Quiet!" said the Queen. "I do not want the dear kind." (6)
9. "We want to see the handsome Indian bow," said the squaws. (5)
10. The old sultan decided to give his harp. (3)

40 Stargazing

MIKE SHENK

This truly is a four-star puzzle. Hidden in this matrix of crossing lines are four regular, five-pointed stars. In each case, the outline of the star is complete and without breaks. How many of them can you find?

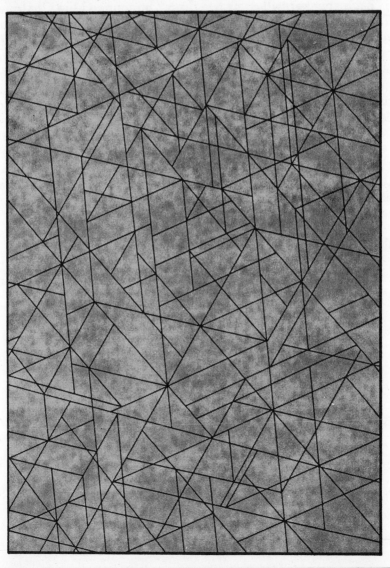

41 Six Discs

ROBERT GRAY

Mr. Allen, Ms. Barr, and Mr. Conn were scheduled to speak at the Solvers' Club. The Chairman introduced them, and then held up a bag containing six discs numbered 1 through 6.

"Each speaker will draw two discs," announced the Chairman. "The guest with the highest total will take the podium first, the one with the next highest total will be second, and the one with the lowest total will be last. If two or more guests have the same total, the one with the highest numbered disc will take precedence."

Mr. Allen drew first. He looked at his two numbers and said, truthfully, "I can possibly be first and I can possibly be second." Ms. Barr drew next, and said, truthfully, "I can possibly be second and I can possibly be third." Mr. Conn then came from the back of the hall, not having heard the preceding, and drew the remaining discs. He made no comment. The Chairman said, "Mr. Allen said he could possibly be second or third. Then Ms. Barr said she could possibly be first or second. Have you no comment?"

Mr. Conn looked at his two numbers. "Yes," he said. "There is a mistake somewhere."

"My apologies," said the Chairman. "I interchanged the comments. It was Mr. Allen who said he could be first or second, and then Ms. Barr who said she could be second or third."

What numbers did each person draw?

42 Ad Infinitum

K.M. PASKERT

Times are tough all over, and everyone—including the famous—is looking for extra income. In fact, the Position Wanted section of classified ads reprinted below is full of ads placed by celebrities of fact and fiction. If you can identify all ten advertisers, classify yourself as an expert.

SAILOR needs job, will consider wrk with canning co as spinach taster. Write BOX P.

JOLLY, slightly overwt man seeks off-season wrk, has own transp but must park on roof. BOX SC.

TRIO seeks constrctn wrk, experts w/ sticks, straws, bricks. Write BOX TLP.

ONE-TIME chf exec must find new job, will work for peanuts. BOX JC.

COUPLE let go frm prev position due to misunderstanding. Have exp at gardening, apple-polishing, snake-sitting. Write BOX A/E.

DASHING magnetic man seeks nighttime wrk, must be finished by dawn. BOX CD.

RETIRING at end of yr, seeking 2nd career, able to use scythe. Write BOX FT.

MUCH-TRAVELED man seeks moonlighting positn, desires small step in responsblty, giant leap in salary. Write BOX NA.

TALENTED kids seek wrk during vactn, great at putting on shows. Dog incl. BOX TLR.

WOMAN seeks job as bareback rider for circus, etc. Much prev exposure. BOX LG.

43 Mindet a Helyére!
Timed Criss-Cross Puzzle

Mindet a helyére," we're told, is Hungarian for "all is correct." That was the title of a puzzle competition at an International Socialist Congress of Puzzle Editors held in Hungary. To solve (you don't need to know Hungarian), simply complete the crossword using the words listed by length at right. Ignore diacritical marks.

Expert's time: 9 minutes.

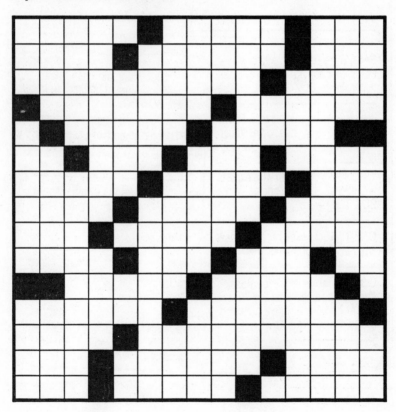

THE FOUR-STAR PUZZLER

2 Betűsek
AD
EK
ES
HT
RA
US

3 Betűsek
ALÁ
ARI
ATA
ATI
GÓR
IMÁ
KAS
KOS
LOS
NÁD
PÁL
PUN
STB
TON

4 Betűsek
ACTA
ÁROK
DELI
FURA
KARD
KEPE
KOPT
LIMA
ÓCSA
OLOM
OSZT
RITE
SZAK
TITO
VESI
ZIZI
ZOLA
ZOLI

5 Betűsek
ALAKI
ASÓKA

CSEKA
DOROG
DOSZT
DUCOL
DULCE
FUCCS
GOGOL
HALEB
IROTA
KACSA
KASZT
KÖRIT
KULCS
LISTA
PUCCS
RECCS
SIITA
SZIKH
SZITA
TARCA
TEREL
TORZS
TOSCA
TÓSZT

6 Betűsek
AZIMUT
ELOSZT
FELRAK
LUSAKA
ODAADÓ
SZÓLAM

7 Betűsek
AKARATI
VOSZTOK

8 Betűsek
FELEMELÓ
FONOTÉKA
KULLANCS
SARASATE

9 Betűsek
PALATINUS
STARTOLÁS

10 Betűsek
EGÉSZSÉGES
STERILIZÁL

44 Who's in Love?

NANCY SEKAC

The names of some of the lovers below have been linked for centuries, but never so thoroughly as here. Can you find the pair of lovers whose names are hidden from left to right in each row of letters? For example, the first row of letters contains the names ROMEO and JULIET.

Ex. JURLIOMEETO *Romeo and Juliet*

1. CPUSPYCIHED _____

2. CBLONYNDIEE _____

3. HABELOELAIRSED _____

4. TAJARNZANE _____

5. CANTLEOPONATRAY _____

6. BAKERBINE _____

7. JOYOHKON _____

8. SADELMISLOAHN _____

9. JOFHRNANKINYE _____

45 Can You Answer This? III

HENRY HOOK

For those of you who pride yourselves on your learning, here are some questions to test your knowledge of things musical.

1. In the "Peanuts" comic strip, young Schroeder believes Beethoven to be the greatest composer ever. But whom did Beethoven consider to be the greatest composer ever?

2. During the years 1917–1940, the Metropolitan Opera House showed a record number of performances of *The Marriage of Figaro*. How many?

3. When offered the post of organist at Versailles, Mozart declined. Why?

4. What is literally unique about Chopin's *Étude for Piano in G-Flat Major*?

5. John Cage's 1953 work *Imaginary Landscape No. 4* never sounds the same way twice. It is scored for 12 of what type of "musical instrument"?

6. Who was Max Yasgur?

7. Sad songs move you to tears. Statistically, are you probably a man or a woman?

8. True or false: Whistling attracts honeybees.

9. During a performance of Wagner's *Die Meistersinger* in West Germany, the audience watched the singers mouth their parts, emitting no sound. How come?

10. What are the una corda, the sostenuto, and the damper?

11. A ballet dancer preparing to perform in *Swan Lake* should stock up on something. What?

12. In pop music jargon, what's a "stiff"?

13. According to the lyric, who played tenor saxophone in "Jailhouse Rock"?

14. Before achieving their respective TV successes, what did both Raymond Burr and Robert Conrad do for a living?

46 Lawn Order
Logic Problem

LEIGH KING

The five neighbors along the west side of the 400-block of North Windsor Drive take pride in both their beautiful lawns and the spirit of co-operation they share. Each family has an important lawn tool that all the rest borrow, and each possesses a skill or talent that all the others rely on for assistance. All the lawns are unique and distinctive in some particular.

From the following clues, match the names of the families (Vernon, Wright, Xavier, Young, and Zeller) with their addresses (401, 403, 405, 407, and 409, from south to north), the tools they contribute (edger-trimmer, hedge clippers, mower, seeder-fertilizer, and sprinkler), the talents they share (boys to mow lawns, "green thumb," landscape architect, soils expert, and tree trimmer), and the details that make each lawn noteworthy (fish pond, flower beds, fountains, hedges, and ornamental trees).

CLUES

1. When the first block party of last year was held at 407, the guests arrived in this order: the Wrights, the people from the north end of the block, the ones with the fountains in their yard, and the tree trimmer.

2. The Xaviers usually trim and edge along their property lines on both sides—those being the properties of the family who own the seeder-fertilizer and the family with the boys who usually push the mower (which belongs to the soils expert).

3. The Zellers' ginkgo and devil's walkingstick are the envy of the neighborhood, the landscape architect's fantails and black mollies are frequent prizewinners, and the sprinkler owners' calendulas and anemones are often given to neighbors.

4. The Youngs' fancifully shaped hedges often require them to borrow clippers from their next-door neighbors.

5. There are two houses between the Vernons and the family that owns the edger-trimmer.

6. Only the wife at 403 has a "green thumb," her husband being kept busy working on the plumbing for their fountains.

7. The flower beds are located in the yard between the Xaviers and the mower owners.

8. The Zellers live on one corner and the owners of the hedge clippers live on the other.

★ ★ ★ ★

47 Aunt Hildegarde III

DAVID DIEFENDORF

Last time I visited Aunt Hildegarde, she was partial to tea but not coffee, planes but not trains, Pete Rose but not Reggie Jackson—and all because her fancy had been caught by words having *homophones* (tea/tee, planes/plains, etc.). This month she's been spending a lot of time with Uncle Frank, and she's developed a whole new set of likes and dislikes. Can you figure out what principle is guiding her current tastes?

This month Aunt Hildegarde likes to dress in STRIPES, not in POLKA DOTS.

She's wearing SHOES, but not SOCKS.

She enjoys WHIST, but not BRIDGE.

She goes to the RACES, but she doesn't like HORSES.

She's taken up POTTERY, and she's given up KNITTING.

She's fond of her new pet HYENA, but she's lost interest in her PARROT.

She likes TRUTH but not LIES.

She likes an ORANGE but not an APPLE.

She'll get DRUNK but not SMASHED.

She plans to vacation in ATHENS, even though she hates GREECE.

48 Small Concerns

VIRGINIA C. McCARTHY

Minutius Pore, a folklore specialist, had oft noted and been troubled by the cloud of obscurity and misinformation surrounding the dwarfs in *Snow White and the Seven Dwarfs*. Grimm had referred to the dwarfs only as the first through the seventh dwarf; and then a tasteless twentieth century had belittled them with names like Doc and Dopey. So, stirred by righteous indignation and the indefatigable curiosity of a researcher, Minutius undertook a thorough study of Snow White's milieu. The results of his study were unexpectedly rewarding—he found records not only of the dwarfs' full names, but of their heights and weights as well! He unearthed fragments of a list of dwarf data and was able to reconstruct what is shown below. (Since in the dwarfs' time and place weight was not the matter of concern that it is today, their weights were rounded off to the nearest 5 kilograms; but their heights were recorded to the nearest centimeter.) Minutius also ferreted out several notes written by the dwarfs—all were in an excellent state of preservation, but none was fully signed, and one had the entire signature missing. The notes revealed, among other things, that the dwarfs were clever with numbers. From the partially restored list and the dwarfs' notes, Minutius began by listing the dwarfs' first names (Felix, Franz, Hans, Heinrich, Johann, Karl and Wolfgang) and last names (Baumann, Baumgarten, Baumhaus, Applebaum, Lindenbaum, Tannenbaum, and Baum), and then proceeded to reconstruct the full names, heights, and weights of all seven dwarfs! Can you do the same?

Dwarf Data		
Hans		
Heinrich		50 kg.
	Applebaum	35 kg.
	Lindenbaum	45 kg.
	Baum	40 kg.
	Baumann	
		120 cm.

DWARF NOTES

1. All of us, except poor Felix, are more than 120 centimeters tall, and only Franz weighs less than 40 kilograms.

2. None of us reached a height of 140 centimeters (alas), but as the tallest my height is three times as much in centimeters as Baumgarten's weight is in kilograms.—Baumhaus.

3. Karl's height is the product of two consecutive numbers and Franz's height is a perfect cube, but my height is pretty much of a numerical loser.—Baum

4. No more fressing on bratwurst, Wolfgang! If you don't control your greed you'll soon weigh 100 kilos! As it is, your weight is a multiple of 12. Tannenbaum, with his passion for knockwurst, is almost as bad—but at least his weight isn't divisible by a number as big as 12 (unless you divide it by one, silly!). —Johann

P.S. I may be the third shortest, but I still get hungry.

5. Now look here, Johann! Since my height and Tannenbaum's are not divisible by any number at all (yes, we know you don't divide by one!*#!!#*), we need *some* consolation! Anyway, I'm the third tallest!—Wolfgang

49 Brinksmanship, or the Mexican Standoff

J.F. PEIRCE

While cruising in an unmarked police car, Marks and Engels (two detectives who had been assigned as a team because of their names) came upon five men and a woman holding guns on each other in a "Mexican standoff." All six wore official Brink's uniforms.

The road had been sprinkled with roofing nails, and a Brink's armored truck with four flat tires was in a ditch nearby. Behind it was a stolen car whose license number had just come over the police radio. According to the police report, the car had been stolen by three unidentified members of the Society of the Forked Tongue, a peculiar cult whose members *always* lied, whatever the circumstances.

Marks and Engels got the drop on the six and disarmed them.

Three of them—Moe, Larry, and Curly—claimed to be Brink's guards who'd been surprised by the other three—Peter, Paul, and Mary—when their truck had gone into the ditch. Fortunately, they said, they'd been able to draw their own guns and set up the standoff.

Peter, Paul, and Mary maintained that *they* were the Brink's guards and that Moe, Larry, and Curly had waylaid *them*.

Marks and Engels knew that they could call the armored-car company and learn which were the holdup men, but it would be a feather in their fedoras, they felt, if they could figure out the answer themselves.

"Let's question them," Marks said to Engels. "The good guys are bound to tell the truth, and the bad guys are bound to lie."

Engels nodded and took out his pen and notebook to jot down everyone's answers.

Marks turned to Moe. "Why should we believe you?" he demanded.

"Because I've been telling you the truth," Moe replied.

"He's a liar!" Peter shouted.

"Baloney!" exploded Larry, pointing at Peter. "*He's* the liar!"

Paul stepped forward. "You're the liar," he sneered at Larry. "Your statement is as false as your teeth."

Engels noted that Larry did indeed have false teeth.

"What's the use?" moaned Curly. "None of us is going to admit being a criminal."

"I'd admit it as quickly as you if it were the truth," said Mary, "but it's not."

"Stop it!" Marks commanded. "Stop! We know which of you are guards and which of you are robbers."

"We do?" Engels said, obviously puzzled. "Which are which?" How did Marks know?

★ ★ ★ ★

50 Words in Common

N.M. MEYER

The words in each set below are incomplete. Can you figure out what shorter word is missing from the words in each set?

1. UNCH
   SHERN
   CURIER
   BIQUE

3. ATD
   INSE
   USIL
   LAT

2. TAN
   CON
   CHER
   STLE

4. COLL
   MY
   HST
   CORT

THE FOUR-STAR PUZZLER

51 News from Abroad, Hardcase?
Three-Minute Detective

ROBERT L. LIDDIL

Inspector, I've got four people covering this area and they work independently. It disturbs me that I keep hearing that one of them is doing his legwork only as far as the hotel bar, and I can't find out which. My rewrite people are upset because they have to make a composite from all four correspondents' stories and they don't know what to include and still retain credibility." Editor W. C. Black of World News Service dropped four manuscripts on Hardcase's desk. "Can you help by looking at these?"

"A little out of my official jurisdiction, I'm afraid," said Hardcase, picking up the news releases reluctantly.

"It's fraud," Black argued.

"My badge doesn't carry any weight on the other side of the world," Hardcase answered as he skimmed the lead paragraphs of the four stories.

"No, but I can fire the loafer when I learn who he is," Black said, "even halfway around the world."

Hardcase nodded and resumed reading.

Joe Short's dispatch said "Burnooses and kepis are inadequate to turn the fury of the simoom from the suffering column of fleeing Hindus."

Earl Burton's read more lyrically: "Like a muezzin calling the faithful to prayer, the fierce wind keened in the ears of the long line of Sind evacuees as they wended up the rocky trail."

Donald Meek's story related: "Long columns of pitiful refugees make their way across the desert with a blazing noonday sun beating down on their heads and a violent sandstorm obscuring landmarks only a meter distant."

The final piece, by Mark Wright, began: "The scream of jets and shells overhead is drowned by the howl of the wind through the narrow pass as thousands of terrified peasants hurry to escape their ravaged farms and villages."

Hardcase looked sourly at the anxious editor. "Why not save some money and do the reading public a favor at the same time? Fire them all. This is atrocious writing."

"I know," Black answered with a shrug. "That's what rewrite is for. But can you tell me who's faking his reports?"

"I think so," Hardcase replied, handing Black the phony story. Whose report did Hardcase conclude had been written from the comfort of a hotel cocktail lounge?

★ ★ ★ ★

52 Novel Collaborations
ED STEIN

I wonder if you were aware that Henry James and D.H. Lawrence once collaborated on a novel. Impossible, you say? Why, not at all—the result was *Portrait of a Lady Chatterley's Lover*. This book is just one of many products of literary teamwork; another is the adventure story by Ernest Hemingway and Jack London: *The Old Man and the Sea Wolf*. Below are listed the authors of several more such works (the number in parentheses indicates how many words are in the title). See if you can name all of these collaborative novels.

1. John Steinbeck & Jonathan Swift (4)

2. Thomas Hardy & Richard Wright (6)

3. Nikolai Gogol & Norman Mailer (6)

4. Henrik Ibsen & Jack London (6)

5. D.H. Lawrence & Ivan Turgenev (5)

6. Graham Greene & G.B. Shaw (5)

7. Joseph Conrad & Arthur Koestler (5)

53 Figuratively Speaking

ANN STONE

This puzzle, a literary logic test on figures of speech, is by far the most enjoyable, thought-provoking, educational quiz ever invented. (Cut the hyperbole, right?) Okay, match the 15 types of figures of speech below (numbered 1–15) with the examples at the bottom of the page. To make your job easier, we've used the definitions and examples exactly as they appear in *Webster's Third New International Dictionary*. If you can correctly complete this complex quiz, consider yourself a clever cogitator. (*That's* alliteration.)

Definitions

____ **1. ANADIPLOSIS** (AN-uh-di-PLOH-sis) Repetition of a prominent word, usually the last in a phrase, clause, sentence or verse, at the beginning of the next phrase, clause, sentence or verse.

____ **2. APOSIOPESIS** (AP-uh-SIGH-uh-PEE-sis) The leaving of a thought explicitly incomplete in writing or speaking often by a sudden breaking off and shifting grammatical construction for rhetorical purposes.

____ **3. CHIASMUS** (kigh-AZ-mus) The inversion of the order of syntactical elements in the second of two juxtaposed and syntactically parallel phrases or clauses.

____ **4. EPANORTHOSIS** (EP-uh-nor-THOH-sis) A substitution of a more emphatic word or phrase for one just preceding.

____ **5. HENDIADYS** (hen-DIGH-uh-dis) The expression of an idea by two nouns connected by "and" instead of by a noun and adjective.

____ **6. HYSTERON PROTERON** (HISS-tuh-ron PROT-uh-ron) A figure of speech consisting of reversal of a natural or rational order.

____ **7. LITOTES** (LIGH-tuh-teez) Understatement in which an affirmative is expressed by the negative of the contrary.

____ **8. MALAPROPISM** (MAL-uh-prop-is-um) A humorous misapplication of a word or phrase; a blundering use of a word that sounds somewhat like the one intended but is ludicrously wrong in the context.

____ **9. OXYMORON** (OCK-si-MOHR-on) A combination for epigrammatic effect of contradictory or incongruous words.

____ **10. PARALEIPSIS** (PAIR-uh-LIPE-sis) A passing over with brief mention in order to emphasize rhetorically the suggestiveness of what is omitted.

_____ **11. PLEONASM** (PLEE-uh-naz-um) Iteration or repetition in speaking or writing; the use of more words than those necessary to denote mere sense.

_____ **12. PLOCE** (PLOH-see) Emphatic repetition of a word with particular reference to its special significance.

_____ **13. POLYSYNDETON** (POL-ee-SIN-di-ton) Repetition of conjunctions in close succession.

_____ **14. SYLLEPSIS** (si-LEP-sis) The use of a word (as an adjective or verb) in grammatical agreement with only one of two nouns by which it is governed.

_____ **15. WELLERISM** (WELL-ur-iz-um) An expression comprising a well-known quotation followed by a facetious sequel.

Examples

A. "Saw with his own eyes."

B. "Cups and gold."

C. "As headstrong as an allegory on the banks of the Nile."

D. "He's not a bad ballplayer."

E. "A wife who was a wife indeed."

F. "I remain well and my wife also."

G. "Most brave, nay, most heroic act."

H. "'Every one to his own taste,' said the old woman as she kissed the cow."

I. "Then came the thunder and lightning."

J. "Rely on his honor—honor, such as his?"

K. "His behavior was—but I blush to mention that."

L. "Cruel kindness."

M. "A superman in physique but in intellect a fool."

N. "We have ships and men and money and stores."

O. "I confine to this page the volume of his treacheries and debaucheries."

THE FOUR-STAR PUZZLER

54 Trivia Quiz

DOUG and JANIS HELLER

Here's a special workout for puzzlers who pride themselves on knowing a wide range of facts.

1. Place in chronological order:
   a. The discovery of Pluto
   b. The invention of the lightbulb
   c. The Battle of Wounded Knee
2. Who composed "Onward Christian Soldiers"?
3. The Wizard lived in the land of Oz. Who is the most famous resident of Uz?
4. In the Aesop fable about the tortoise and the hare, which animal was chosen to be the judge?
5. When Argus slept, how many of his eyes did he close?
6. In 1893, what country became the first to grant women the right to vote?
7. Who introduced potatoes to Ireland?
8. Who said, "I do not take drugs. I am drugs"?
9. When a waiter calls out "82," what have you asked for?
10. In 1927, Charles Lindbergh was the first to receive this title. What title?
11. What shape is the Blarney Stone?
12. Name all Shakespearean tragedies set in Venice.
13. Whose name means "pine seed" in Italian?
14. A witness said that because the moon was high, he could easily see Duff Armstrong commit murder. Who was the defense attorney who freed his client by producing an almanac that showed that on that night the moon was actually low?
15. What was the final spoken word in the last episode of the TV show *M*A*S*H*?
16. Name the witch who caught Tam O'-Shanter's eye in the Robert Burns poem.
17. Complete this Truman Capote quote: "I can't recite the ___; at least, not correctly."
18. Which American newspaper was the first to have a Sunday comics section?
19. A griffin is half lion, half eagle. Name the parts of a chimera.
20. What world leader tried out for the Washington Senators baseball team?

21. In the song "Waltzing Matilda," the jolly swagman sat beside the billabong, under what tree?
22. About whom was Olivier speaking when he said, "I've learned more about acting from watching him than in any other way"?

★ ★ ★ ★

55 We Get Letters...

MIKE SHENK

Can you determine what letter is next in each of the sequences below?

1.	A	D	G	J	M	P	_____
2.	B	C	D	E	G	P	_____
3.	Q	W	E	R	T	Y	_____
4.	B	C	D	E	H	I	_____
5.	S	M	T	W	T	F	_____
6.	S	T	U	P	E	F	_____
7.	A	E	I	M	Q	U	_____
8.	A	E	F	H	I	K	_____

THE FOUR-STAR PUZZLER

Cryptography I
SALLY PORTER

Each of these messages has been put into a simple substitution letter code. The substitutions are constant throughout each cipher, but change from one sentence to the next. An asterisk indicates a proper name.

56 Tempus Fugit

TSRDTNGTI RTWIOL LTK BTNNGOP BOV IGCO
IYVUON. ATUUGLM LBTNR—TIOSL TVLAON, "GR
YVIK LOOBL IYVUON."

57 Size-Wise

DR DK YBR YVLVKKMZDWC RZFV RSMR PBBJ
RSDYPK LBGV DY KGMWW TMLHMPVK. KB JB
KFNTBVYMK MYJ DYLBGV RMA QBZGK.

58 Widows' Woes

*QUOTED QUIOSON WHEICAIMERLF REO OUB
FZUB CIHA QSFUNDOD UO *CHAFTED EYFU
GSE GSTAU REFFACCA VYEDAI.

59 Roots

ILK IVDAJBJLH RIL UHXX KDM USIU
PIXXIADDY ILE OILBIADDY UAIRH USHJA
WICJXK UAHH UD USH VILEJRDDU.

60 Battle of the Bulge

INGGTOORGH CHYD BRKKNXTOON FNEIT
FQTOOF UNGVTX RG INORXHT IDNXY. MTFY
FWHQ FQEBRGH HIT IXTNB UTFFTXY.

61 Relative Ages
VIRGINIA C. McCARTHY

A sexagenarian, a septuagenarian, and an octogenarian each had one grandchild. The numerical relations between the ages of these grandparents (whose names were Adam, Nora, and Allen) and their grandchildren (Mada, Aron, and Nella) were such as to leave them all open-mouthed with stupefaction. The average age of the sexagenarian, the septuagenarian, and the octogenarian was twice the age of the octogenarian's grandson, three times the age of Adam's grandchild, and four times the age of the sexagenarian's grandchild; and the average age of the grandchildren was equal to the difference between the ages of Mada's grandfather and Aron's grandmother. From this sentenceful of information, can you match grandparents with grandchildren and find out who is how old? (Everybody's age—and each average age—is a whole number.)

THE FOUR-STAR PUZZLER

62 Battle of the Sixes

N. M. MEYER

To solve this criss-cross puzzle, insert the 54 six-letter words listed at right into their proper places in the diagram. To help you get started, the first word across is BAOBAB.

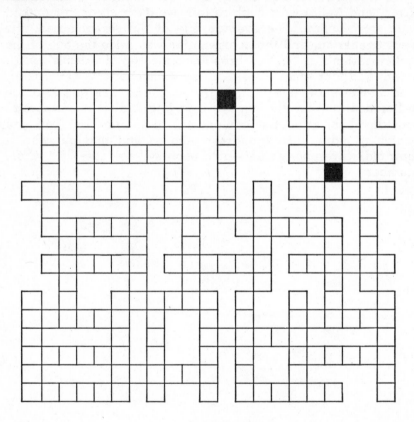

WORD LIST

	COMEDY	GANNET	RANGER
	DECIDE	GOBLET	SETTLE
ACTION	DEFEND	IMPACT	SPIRIT
AFFAIR	DOCTOR	IMPORT	STRICT
AFFORD	EFFORT	LEGACY	SYSTEM
ANEMIA	ELEVEN	MARINE	TABLET
BABOON	EMBLEM	NOVICE	TALENT
BAOBAB	EMERGE	OCTAVE	TARTAN
BATBOY	ENCORE	OUTFIT	THROAT
BEACON	ENSIGN	OVERDO	TICKET
BOBBIN	ENTICE	PARENT	TOTTER
BREATH	ENTREE	POSTAL	TROWEL
BUDGET	ENZYME	PROPEL	TRYING
CAMERA	EXPORT	PROPER	TUNNEL

★ ★ ★ ★

63 An Open-and-Shut Case
FRED BERNARD

A giant gymnasium contains a row of 1,000 lockers, all closed, and a line of 1,000 men. The first man runs along and opens every locker. The second man then runs along and closes every second locker, starting with locker #2. The third man runs along and changes the status of every third locker (if it is open he shuts it, and if it is shut he opens it), starting with locker #3. The fourth man runs along and changes the status of every fourth locker, starting with #4, and so on until all the men have passed by all the lockers.

Which lockers are open in the end?

64 Digititis

B. UPTON-ROWLEY

Most of the digits have been removed from the long-division problem below. Replace the numbers, one digit per dash, so that the completed division is mathematically correct. The puzzle has a unique solution.

```
                  _ _ _ _ _ _ _
           _ _ ) _ 5 _ _ 0 _ _ 9
                  = =
                  _ _ _
                  = = =
                  _ _ _
                  _ 2 _
                  _ _
                  = =
                  _ _ _
                  = = =
                  _ _
                  = =
                   0
```

65 A Shot in the Dark, Hardcase?
Three-Minute Detective

ROBERT L. LIDDIL

The ambulance was in the driveway at 1862 Pleasant Parkway when Inspector Hardcase and Jephro Homer arrived. Homer parked the sedan and rushed up the steps, deferentially holding the door for Hardcase.

Ronald and Dora Simmons, wearing pajamas and robes, sat uncomfortably on the sofa facing Officer McGraw, who had placed his considerable bulk in the dining room doorway to screen from their view the unpleasant business by the kitchen door, one room beyond. A sporterized rifle lay on the coffee table, its bolt open and three live rounds and a spent cartridge lying beside it.

McGraw gave his report as Hardcase glanced around the living room. "The EMTs couldn't do anything for him," he said, gesturing toward the kitchen. "They'll be a few minutes getting things cleared up."

Hardcase nodded laconically. "Have you taken statements?"

"No, sir. We waited for you."

Hardcase brushed past him and into the kitchen. "Any identification?" he asked.

The EMT shook his head as he gingerly removed the larger fragments of shattered glass lying upon the victim's trouser legs. A nippy autumn breeze blew through the jagged hole in the kitchen door's window.

Hardcase returned to the living room and began questioning the Simmonses. "Tell me what happened, Mr. Simmons."

"We'd gone to bed and were almost asleep when I heard a noise on the back porch. I thought it was just a neighbor's cat till the glass broke. Then I got up and got my rifle from the closet. I put a round in the chamber and stepped out into the dining room just as he was closing the door.

"I yelled for him to freeze but he turned and crouched—like he was going to shoot or attack me. I panicked and fired. But it was self-defense, not murder... wasn't it?"

Mrs. Simmons had been nodding agreement while her husband spoke. "That's how it happened, Inspector."

"Then I'm afraid you're both involved... in murder!"

How did Hardcase know the Simmonses were lying?

66 Can You Answer This? IV

HENRY HOOK

You may not know the answers to all of these questions, but think of the interesting additions to your store of useless information!

1. At 7:30 a.m. on January 22, 1943, the temperature in Spearfish, South Dakota was −4°F. So what?

2. He was the first of our Presidents to have a valet, and he refused to move into the White House until it had been completely redecorated in late Victorian. Who was he?

3. What's a "double albatross"?

4. True or false? The person who wrote *A Tale of Two Cities* also invented the mailbox.

5. Was it during the American Revolution or the Civil War that more soldiers won the Congressional Medal of Honor?

6. In 1978, what book achieved the dubious distinction of being the book most frequently stolen from public libraries in England?

7. An addendum to the classic Chicago Fire myth (remember Mrs. O'Leary's cow?) mentions O'Leary's neighbor, Pegleg Sullivan. What did he allegedly do?

8. There's a tailor shop in New Orleans in which the workroom is staffed entirely by blacks. Interesting, when you consider that _____ are made there.

9. In the early 1930s, what person was singlehandedly responsible for a drastic drop in undershirt sales?

10. The words spoken during the first telephone call were, "Mr. Watson, come here. I need you." What words were spoken during the first transcontinental phone call?

11. In 1781, Rene Laennec invented a device with which we all come in contact at least once a year, and many of us complain that the contact is somewhat chilling. What was Laennec's invention? Hint: It enables people to eavesdrop.

12. In 1948, she and her new husband went to a football game just before their one-night honeymoon in Detroit. Shortly after, she was quoted as saying, "I wish I'd married a plumber." Who was she?

13. Most triviots know that the sole survivor of Gen. Custer's army was a horse. But what was the horse's name?

14. Etymologically, which of these words is unrelated to the other four: quite, cute, quiet, coy, quit?

15. How many zeroes in each of the following: a postillion, a mandillion, a silmarillion?

16. Frances Hodgson Barnett gave us what obnoxious literary character?

17. If the Chief Executive of the U.S. dies in office, who are the next three in line for the Presidency?

18. Rank the following coins in value, from lowest to highest: crown, farthing, guinea, shilling.

19. What is or was "Aerospatial 001"?

20. The answer is, "James H. Meredith, on October 1, 1962." What's the question?

21. In Japan, who or what is *Hoteiosho*?

22. "Blood is thicker than water." Yes, but how thick is it—three, six, or ten times as thick as water?

23. This question requires but a two-word answer. To William Shakespeare, who were Gilbert, Richard, and Edmund?

24. During World War II, how could you be sure that a $2 bill was real and not a Nazi counterfeit?

25. Nellie Wilson has a famous son. Name him.

26. In number of sales per year, what company is the world's largest manufacturer of feminine apparel?

27. Do fish cough?

28. A study made by a burglar alarm manufacturer has shown that one particular sound more than any other will scare off a burglar. What sound?

67 3-D Pool

JEFF RUBENS

The grownups wanted to play pool undisturbed, so they sent the three urchins Ned, Ted, and Jed away to another room, giving them pool balls labeled 1 through 10 to keep them amused.

Ned started the amusements by arranging the balls in a triangular shape on the floor, thus:

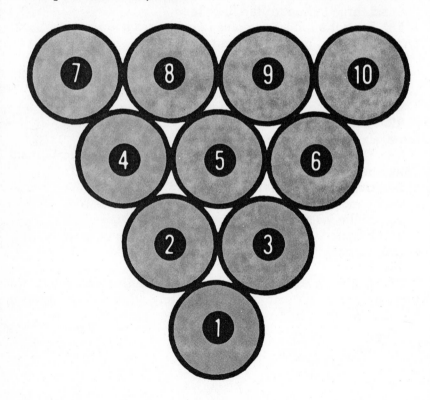

"Look," he said, "The largest difference in numbers between two touching balls is four. I'll bet you can't rearrange the balls, keeping my triangle shape, and make the largest difference any smaller."

Ted moved the balls around for a while, then admitted he couldn't.

"But your shape isn't exciting enough," complained Ted. He placed balls 1 through 6 as Ned had done, but then put number 7 on top of and touching balls 1, 2, and 3; then he put 8 on top of 2, 4, and 5 (and touching 7 as well); then he placed 9 on top of 3, 5, and 6 (and touching 7 and 8); and finally he put 10 on top of 7, 8, and 9. Ted had built a pyramid and was proud of it.

"The maximum difference in numbers between touching balls is six," he proclaimed. "Can you keep my shape and make this maximum difference smaller?"

"Yes, I can," said Jed, finally getting into the act. "I can arrange a pyramid of balls with maximum difference of five, *and* I am sure no pyramid arrangement can make it lower."

How can a pyramid be arranged so that the *maximum* difference between any two touching balls is five? And how can Jed be so sure that his solution cannot be improved upon?

★ ★ ★ ★

68 Baker's Dozen

Can you discover the logic in the arrangement of numbers below, and correctly place the number 13?

1   6   8 9   11

  2 3 4 5   7   10   12

Cryptolists

MIKE SHENK

Each cryptolist consists of ten titles, one of songs, one of books, and one of movies, put into simple substitution letter codes. (A different substitution is used for each list.) The titles in each list are all associated with a single person or group of people. Can you decipher the lists and identify the person or group? Hint: Read down the first letters of the coded titles to find the person or group with which the titles are associated.

69 Songs

TSRRIN FCGKMDPBS

HMB'E GCT KS RIZS

ENPFE MBO FLICE

BIDNSQPMB NIIO

EPHJSE EI DPOS

AMASDGMHJ NDPESD

TSFESDOMT

LSDS HIKSF ELS FCB

ELS XIIR IB ELS LPRR

SRSMBID DPQGT

70 Books

IUCFGTID CHQ NGHQZQH

AGX GTMA MUZQ EOUSQ

NHGF HXDDUC OUEV MGZQ

FGGTHCWQH

LGMINUTLQH

EVXTIQHKCMM

MUZQ CTI MQE IUQ

IGSEGH TG

NGH AGXH QAQD GTMA

GSEGRXDDA

71 Movies

ADTIWSY

HYIYTWYGO

IZD XFKB AFHWOZDO

TDFT UWHKYU

CTDHLB

HYTIZ VB HYTIZUDOI

CFQWXB EXYI

OEDXXVYGHK

CYTDWSH NYTTDOEYHKDHI

KWFX Q CYT QGTKDT

72 Blank's Blank

STEPHANIE SPADACCINI

The local theaters seem to be suffering from "marquee madness"—every marquee starts to give the title of the movie playing at its theater, but ends with part of the title of a movie playing elsewhere in town. Can you re-match the halves and straighten out the mess?

1. *The Children's Baby* _____

2. *Gentleman's Night* _____

3. *Tarzan's Complaint* _____

4. *Ryan's Run* _____

5. *A Hard Day's Hour* _____

6. *For Pete's Restaurant* _____

7. *Von Ryan's Agreement* _____

8. *King Solomon's Daughter* _____

9. *Portnoy's Secret Treasure* _____

10. *Rosemary's Express* _____

11. *Alice's Mines* _____

12. *Logan's Sake* _____

73 Cryptic Broadway

DOUG and JANIS HELLER

The titles below are real names of Broadway musicals. Each of these titles can be viewed as a veiled hint, much like a clue in a cryptic crossword, yielding an answer through some sort of wordplay (anagram, homophone, charade, etc.). To illustrate, the play *Shuffle Along* may lead to the answer "Golan" (*Along*, anag.); and *Through the Years* may lead to "eye" (hidden). Note that *definitions* of the answers are not given, just cryptic directions. Now, can you match the titles (1–12) with the answers (a–l)?

1.	*The Sound of Music*	a.	Gigi
2.	*Funny Face*	b.	Martini
3.	*Can-Can*	c.	Lili
4.	*Dames at Sea*	d.	Mangoes
5.	*The King and I*	e.	O'Jays
6.	*Whirl-i-Gig*	f.	Edams
7.	*The Wild Rose*	g.	Leader
8.	*Dance Me a Song*	h.	Ours
9.	*Little Me*	i.	Mays
10.	*Love Birds*	j.	Sore
11.	*What's the Odds*	k.	Cafe
12.	*Watch Your Step*	l.	Wash

74 A Real Gas, Hardcase?
Three-Minute Detective

ROBERT L. LIDDIL

The dispatcher's voice on the radio sounded urgent. "Any unit in the vicinity of Casa Milano, come in."

Inspector Hardcase picked up the microphone of the mobile unit and identified himself. "We're only two blocks away," he reported. "What's up at the 'Castle'?" Casa Milano was a large estate at the edge of town, set well back in its 60 acres and as secure as a fortress.

"Let me give you a phone patch and you can take a direct report from Mrs. DiLucca," the dispatcher said.

After a brief pause and a couple of clicks, an anxious woman's voice sounded on the radio. "Oh, help me! Paolo's gone crazy and locked me out of the house, and he's threatening to kill himself before his business rivals get to him! Come quick and break in and stop him! He'll really do it!"

"Calm yourself, Mrs. DiLucca, we'll be right there," Hardcase said. Even while he continued to talk, Jephro Homer turned the cruiser and sped toward their destination, turning into the long drive just as Hardcase broke contact.

Their headlights revealed a slumped figure seated on the front steps as they halted before the massive house. Hardcase leaped out and rushed to the side of the near-hysterical Mrs. DiLucca.

"You'll have to break down the door," she said. "I tried but I'm not strong enough."

Hardcase and Homer applied strong shoulders to the door, and separated in the hall to search for Paolo DiLucca among the mansion's many rooms. Hardcase found him sprawled across a kitchen chair and the open oven door, an ugly abrasion on the back of his head and gas still hissing past his lifeless face.

He shut off the gas and opened a window to air out the kitchen. "Don't come in," he called to Homer and Mrs. DiLucca. "The gas is pretty strong in here."

Mrs. DiLucca led them to the living room where Homer called headquarters for an ambulance and forensic team. Then he turned in surprise as Hardcase began reading Mrs. DiLucca her rights.

How did Hardcase know Mrs. DiLucca had killed her husband?

75 Continental Divide
A Cryptarithm Puzzle

MIKE SHENK

E ach letter in this numerical cryptogram stands for a different digit from 0 to 9. Use logic and arithmetic to discover the substitutions that will turn the continent names into a correct division problem. The solution is unique.

```
                                    A S I A
                          ┌─────────────────
          A M E R I C A   │ A N T A R C T I C A
                            A M E R I C A
                            ─────────────
                            M I R T R M I
                            S N I A M R S
                            ─────────────
                              E T S N M T C
                              E S E M F R I
                              ─────────────
                                A T M T M F A
                                A M E R I C A
                                ───────────
                                  C M N T R
```

76 Say It with Flowers
BILLIE BUDD AND LEO BLOOM

Recently the question rose: may flowers leave us laughing? We'd been guardin' a stock of silly puns for quite some time (might one say, through the *anils* of time?), but now we've picked a few daffy dillies for your enjoyment. We hope thistle be a quiz to make you smile and relax (smilax?) and have a yucca on us. Simply fill the blanks below (they're in dandy lines in nice prim rows) with flowers of the proper length. If you're not tickled pink—well, that's just the way it gorse!

1. Why did Buddy ___ his guitar? (9)

2. "Is that player a Detroit ___ Tomlin inquired. (5, 4)

3. "Silence is ___ Serling once said. (9)

4. It's a ___ a heavy load if you've got a good donkey pullin'! (10)

5. Heaven's exciting, but I find ___. (9)

6. I like Count Basie, Dizzy Gillespie, and other ___. (7)

7. I ___ for a kiss and she gave me a smack! (5)

8. The moon's pull makes the ___ in tides. (4)

9. How often did ___ cloak for his Dracula role? (10)

10. I've gotten a lot ___ I drank that gin! (8)

11. "Ha ___ body seen my gal?" (6)

12. Do you remember Satchmo singing that great old tune "___ ___"? (4, 6)

77 Literary Characters

BOOKER T. LETTERMAN

I was sitting in the University library the other evening, grading the final exams of my freshman English class. According to some of my pupils, Pip was a card player and Puck a hockey star. Oh, well. These kids say *I'm* out of touch because I recently alluded to "New Wave" as the latest style in coiffures. At any rate, the experience made me wonder how puzzlers might enjoy an unusual literary quiz I've prepared. Below you'll find a list of names, and the well-known literary works in which they appear. Can you match the names with the novels, poems, and plays which feature them?

Characters

a. Eric
b. Heidi
c. Angel
d. Lew
e. Tina
f. Geoff
g. Chad
h. Hera
i. Dean
j. Ives

Titles

1. *The Idiot*
2. *Much Ado About Nothing*
3. *Light in August*
4. *The Rape of the Lock*
5. *Pride and Prejudice*
6. *Little Women*
7. *The American*
8. *Native Son*
9. *The Marriage of Figaro*
10. *The Changeling*

78 Missing Links II

GARY DISCH

The criss-cross grid below isn't quite finished. The 15 letters beneath it can be inserted to form a pattern of common words across and down. Can you find the unique solution?

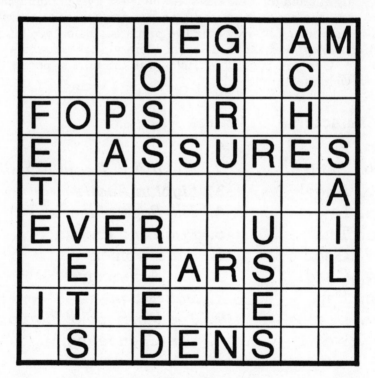

79 Ice Cream Sunday

CHRIS RUSSELL

Poor Wormie Scrubs! On Sunday afternoon, she still had a pretty bad hangover from the party at the High Camp officers' mess the night before. Then five airmen came into the mess for ice cream; they all ordered one scoop at a time, made horrid sounds as they ate, and continuously banged on the table with their spoons. As if that weren't bad enough, not one of them paid for every scoop he or she ate. By studying the clues below, help Wormie figure out what kind of ice cream (Mint Liver Chip, Horseradish Supreme, Chickenfat Ripple, Okra Swirl, and Limburger Royale) was eaten by each airman (Penelope Gumboil, Servile Wart, Perry Utilitypole, Lance A. Boil, and Otiose Bedsore), and decide how much each airman owes.

CLUES

1. By the various airmen, 20, 15, 8, 6, and 3 scoops of ice cream (at 50¢ a scoop) were eaten but only partially paid for.

2. Penelope Gumboil paid for half as many scoops as she ate, and Servile Wart paid for just one more scoop than Penelope.

3. Perry Utilitypole kept screaming, "Silly fat cow!" at Wormie until kicked in the stomach by the airman who paid for 5 scoops of Mint Liver Chip.

4. The airman who ate Okra Swirl either paid for 10 of the 15 scoops he ate, or else he paid for 13 of the 20 he ate.

5. The airman who ate Limburger Royale paid for two more scoops than anyone else, including Perry Utilitypole.

6. Lance A. Boil ate the fewest scoops of all five airmen.

7. The airman who ate Chickenfat Ripple spilled whole pitchers of root beer over both Lance A. Boil and Servile Wart.

8. The airman who ate Horseradish Supreme paid for only one scoop.

80 I Got Rhythm

DENYS PARSONS

I may have a lousy ear for music, but I have a great foot for rhythm! Just show me how the melody notes of a song would be spaced out rhythmically, and I can name that tune. Do you think you can do the same? Each sample below represents the opening bars of a well-known melody; as an extra hint, the general category for each example is given at the end. See how many of these familiar compositions you can identify.

1. ti-ti-tum, ti-ti-tum, ti-ti-tum-tum-tum.
2. bum pa bum pa buddyah bum, Ta bum ta bum ta BOO dum.
3. WONK WONK WONK, WONK WONK WONK, WONK WONK WONK a-WONK.
4. POM POM pa-POM, pa POM POM POM. pa POM, pa POM, pa POM.
5. TUM ti-TAR TAR TAR TAR, TUM ti-TAR TAR TAR TUM.
6. la BONG de BAH-DA
   BONG de BAH
   bottle BONG de BAH-DAH-DAH.
7. t-dum t-DAHH DAHH DAHH DAHH DUMMM tee-um
   t-dum t-DAH DAHHH, doodle-ah.
8. la LOOH ma LOOO-b-la, LOOOH ma LOOO-b-la
   LOOH ma LOOO-b-la, LOOH ma LAH.
9. doo-doodle-doodle-di DUMP-LING, Doo-doodle-doodle-di DAY.
10. ta-da-da-dee-dee, OINK OINK, OINK OINK
    ta-da-da-dee-dee, OINK OINK, OINK OINK.
11. DAH DEE DEE DEE DEE, d-d-DEE d-dah DEE
    d-d-DEE d-dah DEE DEE DEE DEE.
12. b-b-b-BA BA BA BA b-BA b-BA
    b-b-b-b-b-BA BA BA BA b-BA.
13. rip a dip dipadipadipadipadip.

Categories: 1. Classical overture **2.** Ditty **3.** Christmas tune **4.** Carol **5.** Anthem **6.** Sentimental song **7.** Anthem **8.** Folk song **9.** Song from a musical **10.** Waltz **11.** American folk song **12.** Song from a musical **13.** Fiddle tune

81 Acrostic Pun

N.M. MEYER

Each group of letters below will form a word when the missing first letter is supplied. You'll find that each group of letters presents more than one possibility; you'll know if you're right because the first letters of the words, taken in order (top to bottom, left column and then right) will spell out a pun.

___unt	___lower
___enial	___egal
___ust	___round
___iner	___able
___ream	___unch
___oast	___tem
___vert	___erve
___nion	___ease
___hrill	___amper
___ump	___ffect
___tch	___arrot
___imple	___uction
___lone	___oise

THE FOUR-STAR PUZZLER

82 One Word Leads to Another
GLORIA ROSENTHAL

Each missing word in the 12 sentences below contains the same letters as the preceding missing word plus one. The new letter goes on the front, on the back, or inside the preceding word to form the next; rearranging letters is unnecessary.

Ex.: A stray __*cat*__ may occasionally __*cast*__ its shadow in a royal home, but members of the lowest social __*castle*__ will seldom be allowed to enter the same __*caste*__ .

1. During the honeymoon train _____ with his new _____, the groom taught her how to play _____ from a thorough book, although he tried to _____ the lengthy parts.

2. _____ angry fan _____ onto the ballfield, _____ a cowbell in the losing pitcher's ear, and, as long as he was in such close _____, threw an _____ at the catcher, who missed it!

3. _____ anyone who _____ in one of the World _____ knows, a man who _____ a U.S. uniform _____ allegiance to the red, white, and blue.

4. "We _____ so _____ at the wedding that even the caviar didn't _____ me. But I hate to _____ this tale because I am _____ to the bride by marriage," confided the groom.

5. _____ took a great deal of _____ and skill _____ sorcery for the evil _____ in *Snow White* to _____ places with the ugly apple seller.

6. A baseball umpire can _____ on getting many a nasty _____ to a bad call seen in instant _____.

7. In _____ over the omission of the traditional _____ in the store's Christmas crèche scene, the patron demanded to see the _____.

8. "_____ the way," said the _____ at the _____ shop, "I just went on a crash diet, and my car's a wreck."

9. The cadet, having just _____ his appetite by finishing a bag of _____ peanuts, _____ the generals—and left some telltale evidence on his forehead.

10. _____ you know what a _____ _____ while the stag peacefully _____ nearby, or are you another of the _____ of people who can't answer?

11. As the magician uttered _____ invocation _____ waved his magic _____, the light in the theater _____, and he _____ the audience, "Don't blink an eye!"

12. The courts _____ Reginald for the jewel heist since the evidence _____ that he had been in the store that day, but he was _____ when the actual thief was captured.

★ ★ ★ ★

83 Balanced Equations I
THOMAS K. BROWN

Replace the letters in the problem below with digits, one digit per letter, so that the resulting mathematical equations are all correct and balanced.

$$
\begin{array}{ccccc}
FR & + & RAR & = & RFE \\
\times & & \div & & + \\
FE & \times & D & = & BS \\
\hline
DUD & + & DAD & = & RUR
\end{array}
$$

THE FOUR-STAR PUZZLER

84 No Handicap, Hardcase
Three-Minute Detective

ROBERT L. LIDDIL

The residents of Sunny Valley Rest Home weren't exactly unfriendly to Inspector Hardcase and Jephro Homer, just suspicious and apprehensive. But who wouldn't have been, since they were there to investigate the murder of manager Wilbur Rossiter, who had been stabbed thirty times in the chest and back just two hours previously.

Hardcase's intent gaze scrutinized the five suspects assembled in the old-fashioned parlor. George Burke stood erect by the fireplace, blue tinted glasses obscuring his sightless eyes. Beside him Thomas Gwinn leaned heavily against Albert Mangus's wheelchair. Opposite them, on an ornate Victorian couch, sat Frieda Smith and Martha Decker.

"We're all handicapped," George explained, "so it seems unlikely that any of us could have done it. I'm blind, Albert is paralyzed, Tom is a deaf-mute, Frieda is a severe asthmatic, and Martha is deaf."

"Sorry, that doesn't eliminate any of you," Hardcase answered.

"It ought to account for me," Frieda wheezed. "I couldn't exert myself that much."

"And me!" Albert added. "I can't get out of this chair."

"Tom, too," Martha put in. "He's so gentle, he wouldn't swat a fly."

Hardcase turned toward her. "I take it you read lips."

"That's right," she answered, "but Tom communicates only by sign language. If you have anything to say to him, I'll have to translate."

Hardcase turned back to George. "You're not physically impaired," he remarked. "What would hinder you from being the killer?"

"I suppose I could be . . . if I were able to see where to stab," he responded sarcastically.

Hardcase nodded and turned back to Martha. "And your deafness is no assurance that you couldn't have done it."

Martha replied indignantly, "I was nowhere near Mr. Rossiter's office at the time of the killing. I was in the kitchen peeling potatoes when Albert and Tom told me what had happened."

Tom began signing agitatedly, "I saw George go into the office ten minutes before Mr. Rossiter's body was discovered."

George angrily responded, "That's a lie! I had nothing to do with it! I think you and Albert did it because you're both behind on your bills."

Hardcase held up his hand to still the ensuing outburst. "This bickering isn't necessary. I know who the killer is."

What told Hardcase who the killer was—and who was it?

★ ★ ★ ★

85 Writer's Blocks

N.M. MEYER

Each of the groups of letter blocks below conceals a familiar saying. Rotate the letters in each block clockwise or counterclockwise (with the central letter, wherever it appears, remaining stationary) until the familiar saying in each group reads normally from left to right and top to bottom.

1.
```
W N A        I D P        G N I
R A H        N   I        H T R
E E K        N E N        S I G
```

2.
```
E R P        N I D        E A T
T T N        A   E        V E N
C N O        E W C        E C E
```

3.
```
I L S        N   I        I E T
R   T        I T K        H O
O E R        S   E        W H H
```

86 Sevens
A Crossword Jigsaw

N. M. MEYER

The forty words at right, listed in alphabetical order for convenience, can be arranged to interlock in the diagram below. Since all words are seven letters long, you'll have to analyze their letter patterns to figure out how they mesh. Can you find the unique solution?

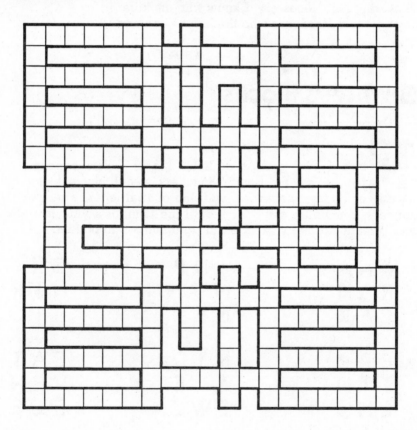

7-LETTER WORDS

ACRYLIC	EXTRACT	OPENING	SENATOR
ATTACHE	IMPETUS	OVERACT	STORAGE
BASHFUL	INQUIRY	OVERJOY	TAFFETA
BROILER	INSIDER	PIONEER	THIMBLE
CHICORY	INSULIN	PROVERB	TURNOUT
CROUTON	INTEGER	QUIETUS	UNSOUND
EMBASSY	ISOLATE	REGULAR	VANILLA
ERRATIC	JEALOUS	RHOMBUS	VERTIGO
ESSENCE	MANAGER	RHUBARB	VINTAGE
ETERNAL	NURSERY	RUBELLA	YARDAGE

★ ★ ★ ★

87 Balanced Equations II

THOMAS K. BROWN

Each letter in the problem below stands for a digit from 0 to 9. Replace each letter with the appropriate digit, so that the resulting mathematical equations are all correct and balanced.

$$
\begin{array}{ccccc}
LB & + & BCD & = & DXZ \\
\times & & \div & & - \\
P & \times & LD & = & LVQ \\
\hline
LXZ & - & VQ & = & VPV
\end{array}
$$

THE FOUR-STAR PUZZLER

Cryptography II
SALLY PORTER

Each of these messages had been put into a simple substitution letter code. The substitutions are constant throughout each cipher, but change from one cipher to the next.

88 What's the Hitch?

AMBLE LEVPAW HVGL, KET SVT DXVPR

XKE RML PG WMD PEFKHT

DXVPRCKDRLH FMRW DNPKHL,

KEXWVH, VH AHKEET JEVRD.

89 Let's Sit This One Out

GLBYK, QKBYK, VKCPR VNBJRQ

NDSKLQV BTMMHN—KPNM PKMWHF.

QRWV—QSRN GRLVTCNQ BRGN KJV,

VSTCOQ FRLVSWLH JKGVCNG.

90 Too Vulnerable?

MGSAFT FLIT UXKBIXGBTI: TETGRSKT

SH NCBSOSBQ UGLRBSRTA MQ

OXKTGK BX KPXD DSHHTGK DPQ

BPTQ KPXCOA PLJT OXKB.

91 Super Bowl

RSTRUVTW XYZVBYZC XVCDERF

VZGUVHTVZH RUURF JK KETGGYUVZH

KVZC, KETGYX GRVEC, HJUHYJTC MTYC.

THE FOUR-STAR PUZZLER

92 I Am the Greatest!

DPCRDMQXPK SXSRJQTRNJB, VBJMQ

VBTH CTFXPK SBXDHWQ,

DPAPTGXPKRO CTBJM VBXJPNM

SQBTDKQ DPJPNXPK CBYKKYNTEXT.

★ ★ ★ ★

93 Letter Imperfect
VIRGINIA C. McCARTHY

When Shortwick wrote to his three friends at the Tallow Club, he not only forgot to write salutations, but he also put all the letters in the wrong envelopes. Upon receipt of Shortwick's letters Nitwick, Pickwick, and Limpwick—feeling vaguely dissatisfied by the contents—each passed the letter he received to another in the group. Still not satisfied, they exchanged letters again, and were—quite rightly—left with a sense of well-being. If none of the three received the same letter twice and if, in the last exchange, Nitwick gave a letter to Pickwick, whose letter did Shortwick originally send to whom?

361

THE FOUR-STAR PUZZLER

94 Can You Answer This? V

HENRY HOOK

Here are twenty questions to see how much you know... or think you know.

1. In 1894, a man named Fred Ott made history when he sneezed. Explain.

2. Would the exploits of William Shakespeare, William Tell, or William the Conqueror be of interest to a toxophilite?

3. Square the number of Zeus' daughters, subtract the number of Heinz's varieties, then divide by the number of a scorpion's legs. What's the result?

4. Would a doctor, a surveyor, or a meteorologist make the best use of a sphygmomanometer?

5. Since the end of World War II, what specifically has happened in London, Helsinki, Melbourne, Rome, Tokyo, Mexico City, Munich, Montreal, and Moscow?

6. Pluralize each of these nouns: talisman, embryo, mongoose.

7. "Zero C" is the freezing point of water on the Celsius or Centigrade scale. What's "Zero G"?

8. In the first act of *Hamlet*, the hero bemoans his fate with the words, "O! That this too, too solid flesh would melt...." In a 1939 film classic, whose too, too solid flesh actually *did* melt?

9. Matrimonially, Presidents John Adams, Zachary Taylor, and Jimmy Carter had something in common. What?

10. Arizona, California, Utah, Oklahoma... how did the 1941 attack on Pearl Harbor directly affect all four of these?

11. "He exists as certainly as love and devotion exist, and you know that they abound and give to your life its highest beauty and joy." What famous seven-word reinstatement of faith precedes these words?

12. In a manner of speaking, German Field Marshal Erwin Rommel and Revolutionary War General Francis Marion differed only by terrain. Explain.

13. It's a soubrette. Do you wear it, play music on it, ride it, or watch it perform?

14. George Washington's picture is on the $1 bill, and Abraham Lincoln's is on the $5 bill. But which of our Presidents is pictured on the $10 bill?

15. The road to the Emerald City was paved with yellow bricks. Where would you be going if you followed a road paved with good intentions?

16. Lillian Hellman wrote *The Little Foxes* as a sequel to her play *Another Part of the Forest*. What was so unusual about this sequel?

17. A tourist in Europe has had his zlotys converted to escudos. Where's he going? From where?

18. A Maryland preacher named Mason Weems created a piece of folklore concerning the quasi-malicious destruction of a woody plant of the genus *Prunus*. Who is the subject of this legend?

19. If you traveled due west from Nashville, Tennessee, into which other state would you cross first?

20. Where will you find the letters C, D, E, F, L, O, P, T, and Z, and no other letters?

★ ★ ★ ★

95 High as a Kite
WALTER PENNEY

Three towns in a rural district are each situated exactly 12 miles from the other two. At a certain moment a kite is flying at a point that is 7 miles from each town. Can you determine the height of the kite in its flight?

THE FOUR-STAR PUZZLER

96 A Strange I. L. K.

ROBERT L. LIDDIL

The five key men at International Lock and Key Corporation were well-known for their preferences and peculiarities. Each had an office on one of the top floors of the I.L.K. Building, and each had a notable private secretary. The men's positions were president, vice-president, board chairman, research director, and sales manager; their first names were Aaron, James, John, Quincy, and Thomas; their last names were Adams, Burr, Hancock, Jefferson, and Madison; their offices were located in 35-S, 36-S, 35-N, 36-N, and the penthouse suite; their individual preferences included long black cigars, cheese Danish, fast Italian sports cars, suede jackets, and bow ties; peculiarities included an abnormal fear of all automobiles, never allowing coffee breaks, donating generously to offbeat charities, never wearing a hat, and jogging during office hours; the secretaries were Miss Grant, Miss Jackson, Miss Lee, Mr. Perry, and Mrs. Pershing.

From the clues below, match names, put each in the right office with the right secretary, and distinguish the preferences and peculiarities of each.

CLUES

1. When Miss Jackson's boss began jogging, Burr would almost bite through his cigar in frustrated rage at the noise coming through his ceiling; the vice-president, who could also hear the racket, would smile stoically and continue working.

2. The man who never wore hats was afraid he would lose his secretary after she became engaged to Aaron's secretary, who worked across the hall.

3. Mrs. Pershing rarely saw the other secretaries as she was usually busy during their coffee breaks.

4. Thomas' bow ties were almost as much a joke among the staff as the president's suede jackets.

5. Adams would turn pale with fear every time Quincy offered to take him for a ride in his sports car.

6. Miss Grant's stony stare and "No Solicitors" sign did not fully protect her easy-mark boss in Suite 36-S.

7. Every time the board chairman stopped in to see Madison, he had to go upstairs and across the hall.

8. At the staff meeting, John personally ushered the others into his penthouse office as they arrived; first the sales manager from 35-N, followed by the man from 36-N, then James, and finally the man from 35-S.

9. The man who liked cheese Danish was in the office directly below research and across the hall from Hancock.

10. Miss Lee worked on the 35th floor.

11. Thomas was envious of Madison's position.

★ ★ ★ ★

97 Cryptarithm

SIDNEY KRAVITZ

Each letter in this numerical cryptogram stands for a different digit from 0 to 9. Use logic and arithmetic to discover the substitutions that will turn the city names into a correct addition. The solution is unique.

$$
\begin{array}{r}
\text{O R L A N D O} \\
+\text{P O R T L A N D} \\
\hline
\text{H O N O L U L U}
\end{array}
$$

98 Humpty and Crumpety

DENYS PARSONS

Look at this!" shrieked Humpty Dumpty. "It's a letter from Crumpety Bumpety, my girlfriend in the next village. I sit on a wall all day; she sits on a committee all day. So we hardly ever meet. Now she writes me a letter and those cads, Tweedledum and Tweedledee, have covered it with broken eggs!"

"What you mean," Alice said, after examining the letter, "is that they have merged the letters of the word EGGS many times into the message."

"That's exactly what I said!" Humpty Dumpty yelled. Not at all what he said, thought Alice, but she puzzled out the letter for him. What was Crumpety Bumpety's message?

```
D G G S A G R S G E L I G N G S E H E U G G S M E P T E Y :
T E S G H G S E K G E G G S I N E G S S H O G R S S E G E S
A G E S N E D G T S S H E G K G E G G S I N E G S M E G G S
N S G A R G E G G S C E G O G M S S I G N G G S I E N G Y G
O S U G R D E G G I S R E C G T I O E G S N . I G G H E G A
E G G E E G E G V S S E A G N E G G A E G G S I N E G F G E
G A S R E G S T H E G G S R E G G S G C O G G S U L E G D B
E G A G G S H O G C G K I E G N G A G C E S C I G E S D E G
N E S T . D O G G S T A G E S K E G G S C A R G E . Y E G G
S O U S R L S E O V G I N E G G G C R G U G M E P E T E Y .
```

ANSWERS

Answers to Wacky Wordies
start on page 368.

Answers to Solitaire Hangman
start on page 370.

Answers to Rebus Cartoons
start on page 373.

Answers to The Four-Star Puzzler
start on page 375.

WACKY WORDIES ANSWERS

1. Teeny-bopper
2. Banana split with whipped cream on top
3. Big man on campus
4. Jack-in-the-box
5. Go off half-cocked
6. World without end
7. Strip tease
8. Spiral notebook
9. Head over heels in love
10. Just between you and me
11. Let bygones be bygones
12. Love at first sight
13. Broken promise
14. Splitting headache
15. Yearly checkup
16. Mixed emotions
17. Hole in one
18. World Series
19. Standing ovation
20. Change of pace
21. A little out of breath
22. Chicken Little
23. Open sesame
24. Round of drinks on the house
25. London Bridge
26. Railroad crossing
27. Round-trip ticket
28. Split-level house
29. Double-decker bus
30. No U-turn
31. Two-car garage
32. *Little House on the Prairie*
33. Electric eye
34. T-squares
35. Ostrich with its head in the ground
36. Top of the morning
37. Middle-age spread
38. Bottom of the ninth
39. Blooming idiot
40. Diet of Worms
41. Weeping willow
42. Shrinking violets
43. Ivy League
44. Pretty please with sugar on top
45. Condensed milk
46. Cut loose
47. Checkout counter
48. Mixed greens
49. The last round-up
50. Three-ring circus
51. Skinny-dipping
52. Curlicues
53. George Burns
54. Heat wave
55. Three degrees below zero
56. A terrible spell of weather
57. Cyclones
58. Partly cloudy
59. Long underwear
60. Man in the moon
61. The whole is greater than the sum of its parts
62. Upper (or high) income bracket
63. Different strokes
64. The check is in the mail
65. Balanced budget
66. Cancelled check
67. Double-digit inflation
68. Short shrift
69. Three square meals a day
70. Corner the market
71. Skating on thin ice
72. Law of diminishing returns
73. Hard as nails
74. Outnumbered three to one
75. Lucky break
76. Calculated risk
77. Rubber checks
78. Clams on the half-shell
79. Safety in numbers
80. Spiraling inflation
81. *The Great White Hope*
82. Sales tax
83. At the point of no return
84. No two ways about it
85. "Tiptoe Through the Tulips"
86. String quartet
87. *Moonlight Sonata*
88. Count Dracula
89. Tally-ho
90. Teetotal
91. Eavesdropping
92. All hands on deck
93. Getting it all together
94. Add insult to injury
95. Spellbound
96. Gossip column
97. *Unfinished Symphony*
98. Get a word in edgewise
99. Hitting below the belt
100. Dashed hopes
101. Cry over spilt milk
102. Start of something big
103. $E = MC^2$
104. Raised eyebrows
105. Round of applause
106. Forked tongue
107. Fly-by-night
108. Negative attitude
109. Way behind the times
110. Writer's block
111. Getting up before the crack of dawn
112. One at a time
113. Till the end of time
114. *Oliver Twist*

115. Square dance contest
116. I before E except after C
117. Short-wave radio
118. Nothing on TV
119. Good afternoon
120. Line up in alphabetical order
121. No end in sight
122. Swear on a stack of Bibles
123. Spread the gospel
124. Split-second timing
125. Hold on a second
126. Day in and day out
127. Better late than never
128. Age before beauty
129. Chip off the old block
130. Receding hairline
131. Light socket
132. Polka-dotted
133. That's beside the point
134. *A Shot in the Dark*
135. Lying in wait
136. Pointer Sisters
137. Pig Latin
138. More often than not
139. Monograph
140. Stereotyped
141. Pineapple upside-down cake
142. Raise a big stink
143. Fourth of July fireworks
144. Side-splitting joke
145. Elevator out of order
146. Home stretch
147. *Tortilla Flat*
148. Narrow escape
149. Full-length mirror
150. Accident prone
151. Dangling participle
152. Stand-up comic
153. Suspended animation
154. Down-to-earth
155. Aluminum siding
156. Search high and low
157. Archenemies
158. Steal from the rich and give to the poor
159. You're under arrest
160. Crime wave
161. Reading between the lines
162. The plot thickens
163. Open-and-shut case
164. An outside chance
165. The inside dope
166. Shadow of a doubt
167. Melting pot
168. Cornerstone
169. One nation, under God, indivisible
170. Equal rights
171. Zip code

172. Little Big Horn
173. Mixed company
174. Above and beyond the call of duty
175. A person after my own heart
176. Light-hearted
177. Thumbscrews
178. Disappearing act
179. Three-part harmony
180. Sitting on top of the world
181. High jinks
182. Panic button
183. Close quarters
184. Flight of fancy
185. Life of ease
186. Word to the wise
187. Three Blind Mice (without their i's)
188. Bermuda Triangle
189. Waving goodbye
190. Turn over a new leaf
191. Space invaders
192. Fancy footwork
193. Mental blocks

SOLITAIRE HANGMAN ANSWERS

BODY LANGUAGE
I. OVERHAND
II. BACKFIRE
III. FOOTNOTE
IV. NECKLACE
V. HEADLINE
VI. WISHBONE
VII. SIDEARM
VIII. FACELIFT
IX. LEGWORK
X. EARPLUG

POTPOURRI 1
I. WELCOME
II. FAVORITE
III. ROMANCE
IV. MYTHICAL
V. ICEBERG
VI. SIMPLIFY
VII. MILEAGE
VIII. VANQUISH
IX. SHOEHORN
X. DAFFODIL

UNDER THE RAINBOW
I. BLUEBIRD
II. REDWOOD
III. EVERGREEN
IV. BROWNIE
V. BLACKOUT
VI. MARIGOLD
VII. WHITECAP
VIII. PINKIE
IX. ROSEBUD
X. CYANIDE

TUBE TOPS
I. DYNASTY
II. STAR TREK
III. BONANZA
IV. NIGHTLINE
V. GUNSMOKE
VI. LOU GRANT
VII. MIAMI VICE
VIII. MAVERICK
IX. PERRY MASON
X. JEOPARDY

POTPOURRI 2
I. DEFIANT
II. BALCONY
III. MERMAID
IV. PERJURY
V. ECLIPSE
VI. MONSOON
VII. HEARSAY
VIII. REELECT
IX. BRUSQUE
X. SUREFIRE

FOR THE BIRDS
I. CARDINAL
II. PHEASANT
III. PELICAN
IV. SPARROW
V. BLUEJAY
VI. PARAKEET
VII. PENGUIN
VIII. OSTRICH
IX. FLAMINGO
X. BUZZARD

POTPOURRI 3
I. INHERIT
II. SCROUNGE
III. DREADFUL
IV. ENVIABLE
V. HERSELF
VI. ARTWORK
VII. WATERBED
VIII. PRETEXT
IX. RAGWEED
X. BRAVADO

FOUND IN AMERICA
I. BUFFALO
II. MEMPHIS
III. DETROIT
IV. ORLANDO
V. CHEYENNE
VI. HARTFORD
VII. WHEELING
VIII. HONOLULU
IX. WICHITA
X. DUBUQUE

POTPOURRI 4
I. GRACEFUL
II. NEITHER
III. SNOWBALL
IV. DISLOYAL
V. SOLVENCY
VI. MAHOGANY
VII. LIONIZE
VIII. BATHTUB
IX. OFFSHOOT
X. PUMPKIN

FEATURED CREATURES
I. BIRDCAGE
II. LEAPFROG
III. GOATHERD
IV. DOGHOUSE
V. MOLEHILL
VI. CATWALK
VII. FISHHOOK
VIII. MOTHBALL
IX. CLAMBAKE
X. FOXHOLE

FOOD FOR THOUGHT
I. PANCAKE
II. MACARONI
III. EGGPLANT
IV. SAUSAGE
V. CHICKEN
VI. POPCORN
VII. OATMEAL
VIII. ZUCCHINI
IX. NAPOLEON
X. AVOCADO

POTPOURRI 5
I. THUNDER
II. FESTIVAL
III. STAUNCH
IV. HANDCUFF
V. PHANTOM
VI. TALISMAN
VII. SUNBATHE
VIII. SYMMETRY
IX. ELEVENTH
X. BAGPIPE

NAME OF THE GAME
I. DOMINOES
II. CHARADES
III. PINBALL
IV. MARBLES
V. CROQUET
VI. PINOCHLE
VII. CHECKERS
VIII. ROULETTE
IX. CRIBBAGE
X. BACCARAT

POTPOURRI 6
I. FEMININE
II. DIAGONAL
III. STUBBORN
IV. VARIABLE
V. LANDMARK
VI. INKWELL
VII. ALMANAC
VIII. WINGSPAN
IX. GUNBOAT
X. LAMPPOST

EXTRAORDINARY PEOPLE
I. PRODIGY
II. SURGEON
III. ADMIRAL
IV. INVENTOR
V. NOBLEMAN
VI. PROPHET
VII. ACROBAT
VIII. WRESTLER
IX. EMPRESS
X. PSYCHIC

SOLITAIRE HANGMAN ANSWERS

POTPOURRI 7
I. SUCCEED
II. BEQUEST
III. GONDOLA
IV. INFAMOUS
V. PLATONIC
VI. LIKEWISE
VII. DOOMSDAY
VIII. CAFFEINE
IX. SANDBAG
X. WHIPLASH

MOVIE REVUE
I. CLEOPATRA
II. SUPERMAN
III. MOONRAKER
IV. FLASHDANCE
V. CASABLANCA
VI. CABARET
VII. GASLIGHT
VIII. EARTHQUAKE
IX. CHINATOWN
X. PINOCCHIO

POTPOURRI 8
I. EXTINCT
II. ABNORMAL
III. LOOPHOLE
IV. MAJESTIC
V. PASSWORD
VI. ROTUNDA
VII. CHARCOAL
VIII. LEEWARD
IX. DUSTBIN
X. SOYBEAN

ODD JOBS
I. MAGICIAN
II. GAMBLER
III. SHEPHERD
IV. EXPLORER
V. BARMAID
VI. ALCHEMIST
VII. MATADOR
VIII. JUGGLER
IX. LOBBYIST
X. HANGMAN

POTPOURRI 9
I. SHERIFF
II. GLACIER
III. INTREPID
IV. BOYHOOD
V. AQUEDUCT
VI. PARTOOK
VII. MAESTRO
VIII. THEREBY
IX. OBELISK
X. DUMBBELL

TAKE A LETTER
I. BEEHIVE
II. JAYWALK
III. PEACOCK
IV. OMISSION
V. ELEVATE
VI. TEETOTAL
VII. EXPEDITE
VIII. SEAWEED
IX. EFFICACY
X. CUTICLE

POTPOURRI 10
I. PROHIBIT
II. BRACELET
III. STRATEGY
IV. SMOTHER
V. ABYSMAL
VI. METALLIC
VII. WITHHOLD
VIII. FOGHORN
IX. LOVEBIRD
X. VIGNETTE

FICTIONAL FOLKS
I. CINDERELLA
II. JAMES BOND
III. DONALD DUCK
IV. LOIS LANE
V. DRACULA
VI. PETER PAN
VII. ROBIN HOOD
VIII. JANE EYRE
IX. DOCTOR WHO
X. DON QUIXOTE

POTPOURRI 11
I. WILDLIFE
II. BREADTH
III. QUIBBLE
IV. REQUIEM
V. STANDBY
VI. TOMAHAWK
VII. VINEYARD
VIII. SUBPOENA
IX. IRONCLAD
X. FOURFOLD

LITTLE CRITTERS
I. SCORPION
II. TADPOLE
III. HOUSEFLY
IV. TERMITE
V. MOSQUITO
VI. STARFISH
VII. SILKWORM
VIII. LADYBUG
IX. BARNACLE
X. PIRANHA

WHERE IN THE WORLD?
I. HELSINKI
II. ACAPULCO
III. BELFAST
IV. RANGOON
V. MONTREAL
VI. CALCUTTA
VII. SHANGHAI
VIII. BUDAPEST
IX. BANGKOK
X. CARACAS

POTPOURRI 12
I. DOMESTIC
II. THANKFUL
III. WIZARDRY
IV. OUTDATED
V. SNORKEL
VI. EUPHORIA
VII. SELFLESS
VIII. CHESSMAN
IX. ASKANCE
X. QUAGMIRE

BIG CRITTERS
I. ELEPHANT
II. WILDCAT
III. GORILLA
IV. LEOPARD
V. ANTEATER
VI. REINDEER
VII. CHEETAH
VIII. GIRAFFE
IX. GAZELLE
X. MANATEE

POTPOURRI 13
I. HOMEWORK
II. REJOICE
III. STIRRUP
IV. DECIPHER
V. FLAGPOLE
VI. VANILLA
VII. TOPLESS
VIII. UPHEAVAL
IX. INNUENDO
X. KNOCKOUT

TRIPLETS
I. PAJAMAS
II. IMPLICIT
III. TOMORROW
IV. LASAGNA
V. WHEREVER
VI. PROTOCOL
VII. ANAGRAM
VIII. ORTHODOX
IX. INSIPID
X. ALFALFA

SOLITAIRE HANGMAN ANSWERS

POTPOURRI 14
I. FORECAST
II. SQUANDER
III. RIVERBED
IV. MOMENTUM
V. PYRAMID
VI. LOLLIPOP
VII. RANDOMLY
VIII. DEVILISH
IX. JASMINE
X. BAZOOKA

AROUND THE WORLD
I. SOUTH POLE
II. WEST INDIES
III. BALTIC SEA
IV. LAPLAND
V. HUDSON BAY
VI. HISPANIOLA
VII. POLYNESIA
VIII. HIMALAYAS
IX. CONGO RIVER
X. GOBI DESERT

POTPOURRI 15
I. ELOQUENT
II. ALTHOUGH
III. VAPORIZE
IV. CAVEMAN
V. NUISANCE
VI. PUSHOVER
VII. CLARINET
VIII. SHAMROCK
IX. PANACEA
X. HYACINTH

TECHNICALITIES
I. CHEMICAL
II. ELECTRON
III. INERTIA
IV. GENETICS
V. EXPONENT
VI. KILOWATT
VII. PARABOLA
VIII. QUANTUM
IX. ZOOLOGY
X. BUOYANCY

POTPOURRI 16
I. DINOSAUR
II. FLEXIBLE
III. DOWNHILL
IV. JACKPOT
V. STOPGAP
VI. UTOPIAN
VII. HOODWINK
VIII. CALYPSO
IX. LAYAWAY
X. SUBURBIA

MORE FOOD FOR THOUGHT
I. BROCCOLI
II. OMELETTE
III. LINGUINI
IV. COCONUT
V. PRETZEL
VI. DOUGHNUT
VII. BRISKET
VIII. CUCUMBER
IX. TORTILLA
X. RHUBARB

POTPOURRI 17
I. ENHANCE
II. UTILIZE
III. SKELETON
IV. ROSEMARY
V. CYNICAL
VI. GOSSAMER
VII. FLYPAPER
VIII. MISNOMER
IX. JOYSTICK
X. PERPLEX

SPORTS TALK
I. PENALTY
II. RACQUET
III. QUARTER
IV. SHUTOUT
V. HANDOFF
VI. HALFTIME
VII. FAIRWAY
VIII. HANDICAP
IX. SEMIPRO
X. REGATTA

AN ACROSTIC
I. ALPHABET
II. NEIGHBOR
III. AFFINITY
IV. CATALYST
V. REPLICA
VI. OBSOLETE
VII. SCISSORS
VIII. TOGETHER
IX. INSIGNIA
X. COALESCE

(1st letter of each word spells the page title.)

POTPOURRI 18
I. LUNCHEON
II. GIMMICK
III. FEATHERY
IV. BLOCKADE
V. GRANDMA
VI. POIGNANT
VII. NEGLIGEE
VIII. SHAMPOO
IX. JUNKYARD
X. YOUTHFUL

IT TAKES ALL KINDS
I. STEPSON
II. ROOMMATE
III. VAGABOND
IV. FIANCEE
V. COPILOT
VI. BUSYBODY
VII. NEWLYWED
VIII. TAXPAYER
IX. PASSERBY
X. FILMGOER

POTPOURRI 19
I. DIAGNOSE
II. THEMATIC
III. WINDPIPE
IV. OXIDIZE
V. ETCETERA
VI. LYRICAL
VII. AEROBICS
VIII. SAPPHIRE
IX. VANGUARD
X. SKYLIGHT

MORE BODY LANGUAGE
I. ARMCHAIR
II. TYPEFACE
III. BAREFOOT
IV. PIGSKIN
V. BUCKEYE
VI. LOCKJAW
VII. KICKBACK
VIII. KNEEPAD
IX. FARMHAND
X. BULKHEAD

POTPOURRI 20
I. COAUTHOR
II. KNAPSACK
III. MNEMONIC
IV. NEOPHYTE
V. PYRRHIC
VI. MUMMIFY
VII. SKIWEAR
VIII. DAIQUIRI
IX. PTOMAINE
X. AVIATRIX

FOR EXPERTS ONLY
I. BROUHAHA
II. HOWITZER
III. RHEOSTAT
IV. STACCATO
V. ZEPPELIN
VI. KUMQUAT
VII. CATACOMB
VIII. CHUTZPAH
IX. BIWEEKLY
X. SIXPENCE

REBUS CARTOONS ANSWERS

1. Omar Sharif (OH-MARCIA-REEF)
2. Toto (TOW-TOW)
3. Wilbur Wright (WILL-BRRRR-WRITE)
4. Cuba (CUBE-A)
5. *Bambi* (BAM-BEE)
6. Hamster (HAM-STIR)
7. Mississippi (MRS.-SIP-E)
8. Assault and battery (A-SALT-AND-BATTER-E)
9. Popeye (PA-PIE)
10. Santa Cruz (SANTA-CRUISE)
11. Sycamore (SICK-AMOR)
12. Lady Godiva (LAID-EGO-DIVE-A)
13. Bob Hope (BOB-HOPE)
14. Fort Wayne (FOR-TWAIN)
15. Gale Storm (GALE-STORM)
16. Real People (REEL-P-PULL)
17. Quiche Lorraine (KEY-SH-LO-RAIN)
18. Ringo Starr (RING-GHOST-R)
19. *Kon-Tiki* (CON-T-KEY)
20. Cole Porter (COAL-PORTER)
21. Egypt ('E-GYPPED)
22. Balzac (BALLS-ACT)
23. Bordeaux (BOARD-OH)
24. *Camelot* (CAMEL-LOT)
25. Parallel Bars (PARALLEL-BARS)
26. Haiti (HAY-TEA)
27. Arturo Toscanini (R-TWO-ROW-TOSS-CAN-E-KNEE)
28. Bingo (BING-GO)
29. Plato (PLATE-O)
30. J.R. Ewing (J-ARE-YOU-WING)
31. Mark Spitz (MARX-PITS)
32. Ty Cobb (TIE-COB)
33. Neil Diamond (KNEEL-DIAMOND)
34. Taipei (TYPE-A)
35. Daisy Mae (DAYS-E-MAY)
36. Hastings (HEY-STINGS)
37. Ramses (RAM-Zs)
38. *A Farewell to Arms* (AFFAIR-WELL-TWO-ARMS)
39. Hercules (HUR-QUEUE-LEE'S)
40. Carol Burnett (CAROL-BRR-NET)
41. Tulane (TWO-LANE)
42. Jack Lemmon (JACK-LEMON)
43. Machu Picchu (MA-CHOO-P-CHOO)
44. Lou Brock (LUBE-ROCK)
45. Yogi Bear (YOGI-BARE)
46. Milwaukee (MILL-WALK-E)
47. *Star Trek* (START-WRECK)
48. Apache (A-PATCH-EEE)
49. Ajax (A-JACKS)
50. Helsinki (HELL-SING-KEY)
51. "Tea for Two" (TEE-FORE-TO)
52. Archie Bunker (ARCH-E-BUNKER)
53. *Auntie Mame* (ANN-TEAM-AIM)
54. Liverpool (LIVER-POOL)
55. Pierre Trudeau (P-AIR-TRUE-DOUGH)
56. Brandeis (BRAND-ICE)
57. Frank Shorter (FRANK-SHORTER)
58. Julius Erving (JULIA-SERVING)
59. "Tomorrow" (TOMB-R-O)
60. Loni Anderson (LA-NEANDER-SUN)
61. Prince of Wales (PRINTS-OF-WHALES)
62. Hank Aaron (HANG-KAREN)
63. Art Linkletter (ART-LINK-LETTER)
64. Minnehaha (MINNIE-HA-HA)
65. Phil Esposito (FILL-S-POSE-E-TOW)
66. San Diego Padres (SANDY-A-GO-POD-RAYS)
67. Scorpio (SCORE-P-O)
68. Amanda Blake (A-MAN-DUB-LAKE)
69. Mozart (MOATS-ART)
70. Sagebrush (SAGE-BRUSH)
71. "Be Prepared" (BEEP-REPAIRED)
72. Chinese Checkers (CHINESE-CHECKERS)
73. *Oh, Calcutta!* (OAK-AL-CUT-A)
74. Peter Frampton (P-TURF-RAMP-TON)
75. Glenn Miller (GLENN-MILLER)
76. Knute Rockne (NEWT-ROCK-KNEE)
77. "Day Tripper" (DATE-RIPPER)
78. Crystal Gayle (CRYSTAL-GALE)
79. Martini (MAR-TEENY)
80. *Can-Can* (CAN-CAN)
81. Algiers (AL-JEERS)
82. Parcheesi (PARCH-EASY)
83. Mistletoe (MISSILE-TOE)
84. Coco Chanel (COKE-OCEAN-L)
85. R. Crumb (ARK-RUM)
86. Beirut (BAY-ROUTE)
87. Dry Vermouth (DRIVER-"MOOTH")
88. Mister Magoo (MISS-TERM-A-GOO)
89. Captain Hook (CAP-TEN-HOOK)
90. Marcus Welby (MARK-A-SWELL-B)
91. Denmark (DEN-MARK)
92. *The Omen* (THE-"O"-MEN)
93. Purdue (PURR-DO)
94. Gene Autry (GEE-GNAW-TREE)

REBUS CARTOONS ANSWERS

95. Bogota (BOW-GOAT-AH)
96. Croquet (CROAK-A)
97. Palestine (PALACE-STEIN)
98. Doonesbury (DUNES-BURY)
99. Mia Farrow (ME-A-PHARAOH)
100. *Portnoy's Complaint* (PORT-NOISE-COMPLAINT)
101. Sonny Bono (SUNNY-BOW-NO)
102. Tarzan (TARS-AN')
103. Kandinsky (CANNED-INN-SKI)
104. Holy Cow (HO-LEAK-OW)
105. Porky Pig (POOR-KEEP-IG)
106. Maximilian (MACK'S-A-MILLION)
107. *Cimarron* (SIMMER-ON)
108. Hirohito (HERO-HEAT-O)
109. Winnipeg (WIN-UP-EGG)
110. Phil Donahue (FILLED-ON-A-HUE)
111. *Sixty Minutes* (SICK-STEAM-IN-IT'S)
112. Y.A. Tittle (WHY-EIGHT-IT'LL)
113. *I Love Lucy* (AISLE-OF-LOOSE-E)
114. Robert E. Lee (ROBBER-TEA-LEA))
115. Boris Spassky (BORE-ISSSS-PASSKEY)
116. Flip Wilson (FLIP-WILL-SON)
117. Cinderella (SINNED-ER-L-UH)
118. Morley Safer (MORE-LEASE-A-FER)
119. Poconos (POKE-A-NOSE))
120. Count Basie (COUNT-BASE-E)
121. *Heidi* (HIGH-D)
122. E.L. Doctorow (E-YELL-DOCTOR-OH)
123. Wyoming (WHY-O-MING)
124. Hank Williams (HANG-QUILL-YUMS)
125. Tungsten (TONGUES-TEN)
126. Lerner and Loewe (LEARNER-AND-LOW)
127. Pennsylvania (PENCIL-VANE-YA)
128. Fiji (FEE-G)
129. Satchel Paige (SATCHEL-PAGE)
130. Fannie Farmer (FAN-EEF-ARMOR)
131. Ilie Nastase (E-LEANEST-OZ-E)
132. *The Caine Mutiny* (THE-CANE-MUTE-IN-E)
133. Roger Bannister (ROGER-BANISTER)
134. Lena Horne (LEAN-A-HORN)
135. Chesapeake (CHESS-UH-PEEK)
136. "Rhapsody in Blue" (WRAP-SO-D-IN-BLUE)
137. Mel Tormé (MELT-OR-MAY)
138. Dionne Warwick (D-ON-WAR-WICK)
139. *The Call of the Wild* (THE-CAW-LOVE-THE-WHILED)
140. *Five Easy Pieces* (FIE-VZP-SEZ)
141. *Superman* (SUE-PERM-ANN)
142. *My Mother the Car* (MIME-OTHER-THE-KERR)
143. *Omaha* (OHM-AHA)
144. "Sweet Adeline" (SUITE-ADD-A-LINE)
145. Beatrix Potter (B-TRICK-SPOTTER)
146. Waikiki (Y-"KEY-KEY")
147. Amelia Earhart (UH-MEAL-YA-AIR-HEART)
148. *I, Claudius* (IKE-LAWDY-US)
149. Arthur Conan Doyle (R-THIR-CONE-&-OIL)
150. Bruce Springsteen (BREW-SSSSSS-SPRINGS-TEEN)

THE FOUR-STAR PUZZLER ANSWERS

1 1. "I'm Just Wild About Harry" 2. "Hello, Dolly, it's so nice to have you back where you belong" 3. "Wait Till the Sun Shines, Nellie" 4. "Michael, Row the Boat Ashore" 5. "I've got a mule and her name is Sal" 6. "A real live nephew of my Uncle Sam" 7. "Where have you been, Billy boy?" 8. "Johnny, I Hardly Knew You" 9. 'Meet me in St. Louis, Louis" 10. "Oh, Susannah, don't you cry for me"

★ ★ ★ ★

2 SirS: If you WanT Your pROoFREADeR bacK, brIng 5 doLLars IN qUARTers TO FunLand PInball ARCADe.

★ ★ ★ ★

3 1. John Ross. 2. Atlantic hurricanes named for men. 3. None—he was long dead when the quote was spoken. 4. To prevent their food from freezing—the refrigerator was warmer than the outside temperatures. 5. Golf. 6. Nothing it touches gets wet. 7. The snow was black. 8. Huge radishes. The event is the Fiesta of the Radishes and occurs on December 23. 9. It's the only work Michelangelo ever signed. He did so after hearing sightseers credit the work to another sculptor. 10. Distinguish colors. 11. Warren G. Harding. 12. He succeeded Alexei Kosygin as Premier of Russia. 13. By getting too close to a skunk. 14. Harrison, 30 days; John Paul, 34 days. 15. Verdi's opera *Aida*.

★ ★ ★ ★

4

S	H	E	R	I	F	F
C	O	A	X		N	A D
R	U	S	T	I	C	A T E
O	R		R		H	T
W		E	A	T		E
D	E	A	C	O	N	S S
	A	R	T		A	C T
	S	T	O	P		S U E
T	H	R	A	S	H	E D

★ ★ ★ ★

5 The Blacks entered at a point from which they could have done the dirty deed, but not at the stated time unless they'd averaged 468 mph—unlikely. Walker entered south of where "Jumbo" was dumped, and in the southbound lanes. He needed no further alibi. This leaves only Dapper and Bullets as the possible killers. Their ticket showed they'd entered far south of the scene of the "littering." However, the ticket they presented at Southpoint was actually that of the accomplice they met at the Midway Diner. Dapper and Bullets had gotten on at Avalon, dumped their "litter," and traded tickets with the accomplice at the diner. (They must have gotten on at Avalon, since a Northpoint attendant would have embarrassing questions for anyone turning in a Northpoint ticket at Northpoint.)

★ ★ ★ ★

6

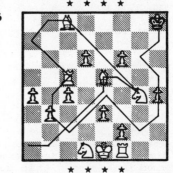

★ ★ ★ ★

7 If the guilty lady were Ms. Pressed, then vase 2 would not contain a properly initialed flower; similarly with Lady Hapramp and vase 4, Mistress Lowdown and vase 5, Miss Twister and vase 6, and Madame Toadrod and vase 7. This leaves only Mrs. Smootha and Dame Diddrem, the latter of whom is proven innocent by the lack of enough vases containing "D" flowers. Thus the high bribe came from Mrs. Smootha; one way to derive her name is to take the O, O, H, T, S, A, and M from the vases in order.

★ ★ ★ ★

8

22	6	25	8	9
5	1	15	2	3
7	4	38 / 28	18	20
23	10	11	13	19
24	12	17	16	21

★ ★ ★ ★

THE FOUR-STAR PUZZLER ANSWERS

9 1. Mar*ch* (cram) 2. Cab*i*net 3. Dam*n* 4. Count 5. *L*ewis Carrol*l* 6. *J* 7. Hammock (*comma*) 8. $1 \times 3 = 3$ 9. $2(3^3) - 5 = 49$; $\sqrt{49} = 7$ 10. *Circle* 11. You're no fool!

★ ★ ★ ★

10

The composers: Bach, Brahms, Chopin, Handel, Haydn, Mozart, Ravel, and Schubert. The instrument: piano.

★ ★ ★ ★

11 Brigett, pixie, dell, hallucination; Eomann, griffin, cave, dream; Maire, leprechaun, tree, chase; Sean, dragon, hilltop, chase; Padraig, unicorn, meadow, chase, real.

★ ★ ★ ★

12 1. HAYD*N* 2. BL*I*MP 3. PAT*C*H 4. FUM*E*S 5. SHA*W*L 6. TODA*Y* 7. B*R*USH 8. FLA*K*Y (NICE WORK!)

★ ★ ★ ★

13 1. Country singers (Cash, Williams, Rogers, Parton) 2. Losers of Presidential elections (McGovern, Humphrey, Goldwater, Stevenson) 3. "Second-generation" performers (Fonda, Boone, Arnaz, Cassidy) 4. Tennis stars (Ashe, McEnroe, Connors, Wade) 5. Film directors (Hitchcock, Brooks, Preminger, Polanski) 6. Cartoonists (Schulz, Kelly, Trudeau, Young) 7. *M*A*S*H* stars (Alda, Swit, Farr, Farrell) 8. Astronauts (Shepard, Glenn, Borman, Armstrong) 9. TV game show hosts (Barker, Cullen, Rayburn, Dawson) 10. Elizabeth Taylor's husbands (Hilton, Fisher, Burton, Warner) 11. Fictional detectives (Marple, Spade, Charles, Chan) 12. *Wizard of Oz* stars (Hamilton, Bolger, Lahr, Morgan) 13. Quarterbacks (Staubach, Bradshaw, Namath, Tarkenton) 14. Miss Americas (George, Mobley, Meriwether, Myerson) 15. Daughters of Presidents (Ford, Nixon, Truman, Smith (Reagan)) 16. "Colorful" surnames (Brown, White, Black, Rose) 17. Olympic figure skaters (Lynn, Fleming, Fratianne, Hamill) 18. Chess players (Fischer, Evans, Capablanca, Spassky) 19. TV title characters (Casey, Grant, Mason, Miller) 20. Famous Jacksons.

★ ★ ★ ★

14 Aunt Hildegarde likes words whose second letter follows the first directly in the alphabet (ABbott, KLeenex, etc.).

★ ★ ★ ★

15 1. EVEN plays an 8 in the lower left corner, setting up a double win possibility (8-4-3 horizontally or 8-6-1 vertically).

2. ODD plays a 5 in the lower right corner. EVEN must play 8 in the center. ODD plays a 7 in the center bottom. EVEN must play a 6 in the lower left corner. ODD plays a 9 in the upper right corner and wins after EVEN plays the 4.

★ ★ ★ ★

16 Twelve, as shown:

★ ★ ★ ★

17 "IMPOSSIBLE BUY SCOTCH WHISKY HERE. PLEASE OBTAIN FROM LONDON FULL INSTRUCTIONS FOR BUILDING SMALL DISTILLATION PLANT TOGETHER WITH GENUINE SCOTTISH FORMULA."

★ ★ ★ ★

18 1. Tom, Dick, Harry 2. Diamond, Club, Heart, Spade 3. Michigan, Ontario, Huron, Erie, Superior 4. John, Paul, George, Ringo

★ ★ ★ ★

19 a. mezzanine b. heighten c. ozone d. bayonet e. postwoman f. tungsten g. falconer h. zaniness i. lioness j. kitten k. softwood l. Fourier

★ ★ ★ ★

20 Robert Fiddler, viola, Bach; Angela Harper, harp, Mozart; Viola Harris, violin, Brahms; Richard Horner, flute, Mozart; Joseph Pfeiffer, horn, Stravinsky.

★ ★ ★ ★

21 1. Chamber orchestra 2. General manager 3. Foster parent 4. Organ recital 5. Golden Rule 6. Martial arts 7. Pearly Gates 8. Sterling silver 9. Master sergeant 10. Nuclear reaction.

★ ★ ★ ★

THE FOUR-STAR PUZZLER ANSWERS

22 1. Rb7 + Re5 (If 1. . . Qg7 2. Bg7 + Kg8 3. Bh6 + Kh8 4. Rh7 mate) 2. Be5 + Qg7. 3. Rbg7 (taking with the other rook also works), any 4. Rg8 mate.

★ ★ ★ ★

23 Uncle Jack's story had several flaws: 1. A hydrometer (which measures liquid density) is not an aircraft instrument. 2. A team of scientists would almost certainly have used a Centigrade (Celsius) thermometer. 3. There are no penguins in the Arctic. 4. In 1930 beer would have been in bottles, and anyhow it would have been frozen solid. 5. The world's first regular TV service was launched in Britain in 1936. 6. Where did the fourth corpse come from? 7. Whatever airstrip Fredericton may have had in 1930 would not have accommodated the seaplane. 8. The telegram from England would have come from the *King*. Score yourself one point for each mistake you spotted; there *are* foxes in Greenland, and Hoover *was* President at that time, so penalize yourself a point if you fell for either of these traps.

★ ★ ★ ★

24

BI	OL	O	GY
UN	CAM	OU	FLAGED
RE	FRIG	ER	ATE
COL	LO	QUI	AL
LEG	ER	DE	MAIN
AR	IS	TO	TLE
OS	CIL	LA	TION
AC	U	PUNC	TURE

★ ★ ★ ★

25

★ ★ ★ ★

26 Our list: upset, tacit, tryst, syrup, spurt, trues, satyr, taste, caste, teach, cache, niche, cheat, aches, strut, strop, ports, sport, rouse, route, routs, pouts, pinup, runic, tunic, satin, trout, spout, unity, pupil, slips.

★ ★ ★ ★

27 This garden is open for the benefit of the public. Please keep to the footpaths and do not pick any flowers.—Rose Madder, Estate Manager.

★ ★ ★ ★

28 Aunt Hildegarde likes words that repeat their first letter.

★ ★ ★ ★

29 1-F; 2-L; 3-J; 4-B; 5-K; 6-I; 7-D; 8-C; 9-A; 10-E; 11-G; 12-H

★ ★ ★ ★

30 *Proverbs across:* Too many cooks spoil the broth; An apple a day keeps the doctor away; Where there's a will there's a way; Time and tide wait for no man; *Proverbs down:* Spare the rod and spoil the child; Many a mickle mak's a muckle; When the cat's away the mice will play; It's a long road that has no turning; A stitch in time saves nine; *Red herrings:* Every cloud has a silver lining; A fool and his money are soon parted; Many hands make light work; A rolling stone gathers no moss.

★ ★ ★ ★

31 In Appleton: Betty and Larry Scarlet, Diana Black's mom, Orson White's mom; Beechville: Anne and John Gray, Clair White's mom, Henry Black's mom; Cedar City: Diana and Henry Black, Larry Scarlet's mom, John Gray's mom; Dogwood: Claire and Orson White, Betty Scarlet's mom, Anne Gray's mom.

★ ★ ★ ★

32 Russia beat Spain, 5–1; Great Britain beat Spain, 4–0; Great Britain beat Russia, 3–0; Spain and Ireland tied, 2–2; Great Britain and Ireland tied, 0–0.

★ ★ ★ ★

33 The note read "Dead men tell no tales." In the code, eighth notes represented the letters A–G according to their position on the staff (F-A-C-E for the spaces, E-G-B-D-F for the lines of the staff, as in music). Quarter notes in corresponding positions represented H–N, half notes O–U, and whole notes V–Z.

★ ★ ★ ★

34 O-clue c.; NO-b.; ONE-f.; NOTE-j.; TENOR-e.; CORNET-k.; TROUNCE-g.; NOCTURNE-h.; CENTURION-d.; COUNTERING-a.; INCONGRUENT-i.

★ ★ ★ ★

35 Perce's answers were: 1. No 2. No 3. Yes 4. Yes 5. Yes (The number is 15.)

★ ★ ★ ★

36 Nine o'clock.

★ ★ ★ ★

37 1. Orville Wright, when he saw the airplane used for warfare (World War I). 2. Nothing. Adult moths don't eat. 3. A man, by about 5 to 1. 4. None. 5. The Pledge of Allegiance. 6. Nadia Comaneci. 7. Boston terrier. 8. The price of gold. 9. 86. 10. One twin is left-handed, the other right-handed. 11. Monk. 12. Lawgivers. (Dickens refused several offers of a seat in the House of Commons.) 13. It was quite a success—it was Mark Twain's *Tom Sawyer*. 14. None—coffee and tea were unknown to Shakespeare's Europe.

★ ★ ★ ★

38 1. Snap, crackle, and pop 2. Red, white, and blue 3. Ready, willing, and able 4. Tall, dark, and handsome 5. Hook, line, and sinker 6. Bell, book, and candle 7. Lock, stock, and barrel 8. Signed, sealed, and delivered

★ ★ ★ ★

39 1. slOW Laps 2. baD OVEn 3. hiS WANd 4. loW RENt 5. drummerS AND PIPERs 6. anotHER ONe 7. sowS WALLOWing 8. kinG ROUSEd 9. bRAVE Now 10. harEM Up

★ ★ ★ ★

40

★ ★ ★ ★

41 Allen: 6, 2; Barr: 4, 3; Conn: 5, 1.

★ ★ ★ ★

42 Box P—Popeye; Box SC—Santa Claus; Box TLP—Three Little Pigs; Box JC—Jimmy Carter; Box A/E—Adam and Eve; Box CD—Count Dracula; Box FT—Father Time; Box NA—Neil Armstrong; Box TLR—The Little Rascals; Box LG—Lady Godiva

★ ★ ★ ★

43

K	A	C	S	A		S	Z	I	K	H		P	A	L
O	C	S	A		A	Z	I	M	U	T		A	R	I
S	T	E	R	I	L	I	Z	A	L		O	L	O	M
A	K	A	R	A	T	I		L	U	S	A	K	A	
F		A	S	O	K	A		K	A	S	Z	T		
E	S		A	T	I		P	U	N		T	I	T	O
L	I	S	T	A		D	U	L	C	E		N	A	D
R	I	T	E		F	U	C	C	S		F	U	R	A
A	T	A		R	E	C	C	S		T	O	S	C	A
K	A	R	D		L	O	S		T	O	N		A	D
	T	E	R	E	L		D	O	R	O	G		O	
S	Z	O	L	A	M		V	O	S	Z	T	O	K	
Z	O	L	I		E	G	E	S	Z	S	E	G	E	S
A	L	A		E	L	O	S	Z	T		K	O	P	T
K	A	S		K	O	R	I	T		H	A	L	E	B

★ ★ ★ ★

44 1. Cupid and Psyche 2. Bonnie and Clyde 3. Heloise and Abelard 4. Tarzan and Jane 5. Antony and Cleopatra 6. Barbie and Ken 7. John and Yoko 8. Samson and Delilah 9. Frankie and Johnny

★ ★ ★ ★

45 1. Handel. 2. Zero. 3. He hated French music. 4. Nicknamed *The Black Key Étude*, the work utilizes only one white key, and it only one time. 5. Randomly tuned radios. 6. He owned the farm where the Woodstock Festival was held. 7. A man, 99 to 1. 8. False. Honeybees can't hear. 9. The singers were on strike. 10. Piano pedals. 11. Slippers. The average performance wears out four pairs. 12. A record that doesn't sell. 13. Spider Murphy. 14. Both were nightclub singers.

★ ★ ★ ★

46 401-Zeller, seeder-fertilizer, tree trimmer, ornamental trees
403-Xavier, edger-trimmer, green thumb, fountains
405-Wright, sprinkler, boys to mow, flower beds
407-Young, mower, soils expert, fancy hedges
409-Vernon, hedge clippers, landscape architect, fish pond

★ ★ ★ ★

47 Aunt Hildegarde likes words that shed their first and last letters to become new words: s-tripe-s, s-hoe-s, w-his-t, etc.

★ ★ ★ ★

48 Hans Tannenbaum, 127 cm., 55 kg.; Heinrich Baumhaus, 135 cm., 50 kg.; Franz Applebaum, 125 cm., 35 kg.; Karl Lindenbaum, 132 cm., 45 kg.; Johann Baum, 126 cm., 40 kg.; Wolfgang Baumann, 131 cm., 60 kg.; Felix Baumgarten, 120 cm., 45 kg.

★ ★ ★ ★

49 Of all the statements the police noted, only one was unquestionably true: Curly's declaration that "None of us is going to admit to being a criminal." (A liar *cannot* say he is a liar.) Therefore Moe, Larry, and Curly were the guards and Peter, Paul, and Mary were the robbers.

★ ★ ★ ★

50 1. Unco*uth*, sou*thern*, cou*turier*, bou*tique* 2. T*artan*, c*arton*, ch*arter*, st*artle* 3. A*ttend*, in*tense*, u*tensil*, la*tent* 4. Colonel, money, honest, coronet

★ ★ ★ ★

51 Only one report contained a glaring factual error that exposed its fraudulence—Meek's. A blinding sandstorm would obscure the sun, even at noon.

★ ★ ★ ★

52 1. *Gulliver's Travels with Charley* 2. *The Return of the Native Son* 3. *The Naked and the Dead Souls* 4. *The Call of the Wild Duck* 5. *Fathers and Sons and Lovers* 6. *The Third Man and Superman* 7. *Heart of Darkness at Noon*

★ ★ ★ ★

53 1-J; 2-K; 3-M; 4-G; 5-B; 6-I; 7-D; 8-C; 9-L; 10-O; 11-A; 12-E; 13-N; 14-F; 15-H.

★ ★ ★ ★

54 1. Lightbulb (1879), Battle (1890), Pluto (1930). 2. Sir Arthur Sullivan. 3. Job. 4. Fox. 5. Never more than two. 6. New Zealand. 7. Sir Walter Raleigh. 8. Salvador Dali. 9. Water. 10. "Man of the Year" (*Time* magazine). 11. Triangular. 12. *Othello*. 13. Pinocchio. 14. Abraham Lincoln. 15. "What?" (Hawkeye trying to hear B.J.) 16. Cutty Sark. 17. Alphabet. 18. *The New York World* (same paper to print the first crossword puzzle). 19. Lion's head, goat's body, serpent's tail. 20. Fidel Castro. 21. Coolibah. 22. Spencer Tracy.

★ ★ ★ ★

55 1. S—every third letter—a simple sequence to start off. 2. T—all letters that rhyme with "tree." 3. U—top row of letters on the typewriter. 4. K—letters with tops and bottoms that are mirror-images. 5. S—initials of the days of the week. 6. Y—stupefying. 7. Y—another simple sequence, this time every fourth letter. 8. L—no curves allowed.

★ ★ ★ ★

56 Actuarial tables say married men live longer. Waggish smart-alecs answer, "It only seems longer."

★ ★ ★ ★

57 It is not necessarily true that good things come in small packages. So do subpoenas and income tax forms.

★ ★ ★ ★

58 Monday morning quarterbacks can now show true misogyny on Tuesday also via video cassette player.

★ ★ ★ ★

59 Any aborigine can tell you that wallaroos and kangaroos trace their family tree to the bandicoot.

★ ★ ★ ★

60 Cannelloni with mozzarella sauce spells danger on calorie chart. Best skip spumoni ice cream dessert.

★ ★ ★ ★

61 Allen, 60, and Mada, 18; Adam, 70, and Nella, 24; Nora, 86, and Aron, 36.

★ ★ ★ ★

62

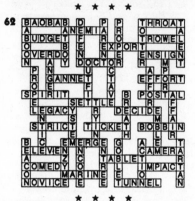

★ ★ ★ ★

63 There are 31 lockers open in the end: Numbers 1, 4, 9, 16, 25, 36, 49, . . . , 961; i.e., all the lockers with numbers that are perfect squares. Reason: Perfect squares have an odd number of divisors, so the lockers with these numbers would have their status changed an odd number of times (leaving them open in the end); all other numbers have an even number of divisors, so the lockers with these numbers would have their status changed an even number of times (leaving them shut in the end).

★ ★ ★ ★

64

$$69 \overline{\smash{)}95980449} \quad 1391021$$

★ ★ ★ ★

65 If the victim had broken the glass to gain entry, it would have been underneath him when he fell, not on his pants. When Simmons rigged the evidence he recognized that the glass would have fallen inward, but he didn't remember to move the body first and then replace it on top of the broken glass.

★ ★ ★ ★

66 1. Two minutes later, the temperature was +68°F.—a record temperature climb. 2. Chester Arthur. 3. Two successive holes-in-one, in golf. 4. False—not Dickens, but another English author, Anthony Trollope, invented the mailbox. 5. Civil War. In fact, the medal didn't exist until 1862. 6. *The Guinness Book of World Records*. 7. He rescued the cow. 8. Ku Klux Klan uniforms. 9. Clark Gable, when he went undershirtless in *It Happened One Night* and started a fad. 10. The same—this time, Bell was in New York City, talking to Watson in San Francisco. 11. The stethoscope. 12. Betty Ford. 13. Comanche. 14. Cute, which comes from the Latin for "sharp." The other four stem from the Latin for "quiet, rest." 15. None—a postillion is a horseman, a mandillion is a loose outer garment, and *The Silmarillion* is a book by J.R.R. Tolkien. 16. Little Lord Fauntleroy. 17. Vice-President, Speaker of the House, President pro tem of the Senate. 18. Farthing (1/4 penny), shilling, crown (5 shillings), guinea (21 shillings). 19. The name of the first Concorde. 20. Who became the first black student enrolled in the University of Mississippi? 21. Santa Claus. 22. Six. 23. His brothers. 24. The $2 bill was the one denomination of our currency that the Nazis never tried to copy. 25. Ronald Reagan. 26. Mattel, which sells over 20 million outfits for Barbie dolls annually. 27. Yes, if their water is polluted enough. 28. A woman's scream.

★ ★ ★ ★

67 One possible solution for Jed, by layers, is:

2 4 8

7 9

3 6

10

5

1

Jed can be sure a maximum difference of five is the smallest because wherever the 1-ball and the 10-ball are placed, there must be some other ball that touches both; if this other ball is numbered 5 or less, it is at least 5 away from 10; if it is numbered 6 or more, it is at least 5 away from 1.

★ ★ ★ ★

68 The 13 should be placed in the lower row. Numbers in the top row, when inverted, can still be read as numbers, while those in the bottom row cannot be.

★ ★ ★ ★

69 "Yellow Submarine," "Can't Buy Me Love," "Twist and Shout," "Norwegian Wood," "Ticket to Ride," "Paperback Writer," "Yesterday," "Here Comes the Sun," "The Fool on the Hill," "Eleanor Rigby"— The Beatles

★ ★ ★ ★

70 *Diamonds Are Forever, You Only Live Twice, From Russia With Love, Moonraker, Goldfinger, Thunderball, Live and Let Die, Doctor No, For Your Eyes Only, Octopussy*—Ian Fleming

★ ★ ★ ★

71 *Vertigo, Notorious, The Lady Vanishes, Rear Window, Frenzy, North by Northwest, Family Plot, Spellbound, Foreign Correspondent, Dial M for Murder*—A(lfred) Hitchcock

★ ★ ★ ★

72 1. *The Children's Hour* 2. *Gentleman's Agreement* 3. *Tarzan's Secret Treasure* 4. *Ryan's Daughter* 5. *A Hard Day's Night* 6. *For Pete's Sake* 7. *Von Ryan's Express* 8. *King Solomon's Mines* 9. *Portnoy's Complaint* 10. *Rosemary's Baby* 11. *Alice's Restaurant* 12. *Logan's Run*

★ ★ ★ ★

73 1-g (sounds like *lieder*); 2-k; 3-i; 4-f; 5-b (Martin Luther King); 6-a; 7-j; 8-d; 9-c (little "I"); 10-e; 11-l (odd letters); 12-h (hidden)

★ ★ ★ ★

74 The critical evidence lies in the fact that only seconds elapsed between voice and visual contact between Hardcase and Mrs. DiLucca. Since the only phone from which she could have called would have been in the house, her story was a lie.

★ ★ ★ ★

75

```
                         1261
1380651 ) 1741054651
          1380651
          3604036
          2761302
          8427345
          8283906
          1434391
          1380651
            53740
```

★ ★ ★ ★

76 1. Hollyhock 2. Tiger lily 3. Goldenrod 4. Snapdragon 5. Hellebore 6. Jasmine 7. Aster 8. Sego 9. Belladonna 10. Hyacinth 11. Zinnia 12. Aloe Dahlia

★ ★ ★ ★

77 Each title has concealed within it one of the ten names, as *The Idiot* literally features Heidi. The full answer list: 1-b; 2-g; 3-e; 4-h; 5-i; 6-d; 7-a; 8-j; 9-f; 10-c

★ ★ ★ ★

78

C	A	B	L	E	G	R	A	M
A		O		U		C		
F	O	P	S		R		H	
E		A	S	S	U	R	E	S
T			O				A	
E	V	E	R	Y		U		I
R	E	H	E	A	R	S	A	L
I	T		E			E	G	O
A	S		D	E	N	S	E	R

★ ★ ★ ★

79 Lance A. Boil, 3 scoops Horseradish, paid for 1, owes $1; Otiose Bedsore, 20 scoops Limburger, paid for 12, owes $4; Penelope Gumboil, 8 scoops Chickenfat, paid for 4, owes $2; Perry Utilitypole, 15 scoops Okra, paid for 10, owes $2.50; Servile Wart, 6 scoops Mint Liver, paid for 5, owes 50¢.

★ ★ ★ ★

80 1. "William Tell" Overture (The Lone Ranger's theme song) 2. "Pop Goes the Weasel" 3. "Jingle Bells" 4. "Joy to the World" 5. "The Star Spangled Banner" 6. "Auld Lang Syne" 7. The "Marseillaise" 8. "Greensleeves" 9. "Oh, What a Beautiful Morning" 10. "Blue Danube" Waltz 11. "Home on the Range" 12. "Seventy-Six Trombones" 13. "Turkey in the Straw"

★ ★ ★ ★

81 First letters read: A gold tooth is a flash in the pan.

★ ★ ★ ★

82 1. Ride, bride, bridge, abridge. **2.** An, ran, rang, range, orange. **3.** As, was, Wars, wears, swears. **4.** Ate, late, elate, relate, related. **5.** It, wit, with, witch, switch. **6.** Rely, reply, replay. **7.** Anger, manger, manager. **8.** By, boy, body. **9.** Sated, salted, saluted. **10.** Do, doe, does, dozes, dozens. **11.** An, and, wand, waned, warned. **12.** Indicted, indicated, vindicated.

★ ★ ★ ★

83

$$14 + 404 = 418$$
$$\times \quad \div \quad +$$
$$\underline{18 \times \quad 2 = \quad 36}$$
$$252 + 202 = 454$$

★ ★ ★ ★

84 The one person who revealed that his handicap wasn't as it was purported to be was George Burke. If he had been blind, he could not have "read" what Tom was signing and would have had to wait for Martha's translation before disputing.

★ ★ ★ ★

85 1. Keeping is harder than winning. **2.** Once an event, twice a precedent. **3.** Strike while the iron is hot.

★ ★ ★ ★

86

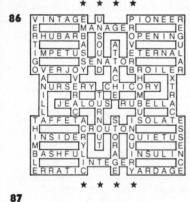

★ ★ ★ ★

87

$$23 + 384 = 407$$
$$\times \quad \div \quad -$$
$$\underline{9 \times \quad 24 = \quad 216}$$
$$207 - 16 = 191$$

★ ★ ★ ★

88 Given enough rope, any Boy Scout can tie up his unwary scoutmaster with square, anchor, or granny knots.

★ ★ ★ ★

89 Rumba, samba, tango tempos exhaust middle-aged gadfly. Soft-shoe routines more apt, thinks youthful partner.

★ ★ ★ ★

90 Bridge game postmortem: Exercise in futility practiced by losers to show winners why they should have lost.

★ ★ ★ ★

91 Aquarium denizens display intriguing array of fluttering fins, fluted tails, gorgeous hues.

★ ★ ★ ★

92 Unblushing titleholder, fresh from boxing triumph, unknowingly bores friends through unending braggadocio.

★ ★ ★ ★

93 Shortwick sent Limpwick's letter to Nitwick, Nitwick's letter to Pickwick, and Pickwick's letter to Limpwick.

★ ★ ★ ★

94 1. *Fred Ott's Sneeze* was the first copyrighted motion picture, filmed by Thomas Edison. **2.** William Tell—a toxophilite is an archery devotee. **3.** $(9^2 - 57) / 8 = 3$. **4.** A doctor—that's the gadget he'd wrap around your arm to check your blood pressure. **5.** The Summer Olympics. **6.** Simply add an s to each. **7.** Weightlessness—zero gravity, to an astronaut. **8.** The Wicked Witch of the West, in *The Wizard of Oz.* **9.** Their First Ladies all had Smith as their maiden names. **10.** They were four battleships that were sunk or destroyed that day. **11.** "Yes, Virginia, there is a Santa Claus." **12.** Rommel was nicknamed "The Desert Fox"; Marion was "The Swamp Fox." **13.** Watch it perform—she's a coquettish maid in a play or opera. **14.** No President—it's Alexander Hamilton. **15.** "The road to Hell is paved with good intentions." **16.** The sequel was written first—seven years earlier. **17.** To Portugal, from Poland. **18.** George Washington, chopping down the cherry tree. **19.** Missouri, for about 30 miles, then into northern Arkansas. **20.** On a standardized eye chart—specifically, the Snellen chart.

★ ★ ★ ★

95 The three towns are at the vertices of an equilateral triangle with a 12-mile side. The center of the triangle is $4\sqrt{3}$ miles from each city. The height of the kite hovering above is the third side of a right triangle in which one leg is $4\sqrt{3}$ miles and the hypotenuse is 7 miles. Therefore, the kite is one mile high. That's a lot of string!

★ ★ ★ ★

96 President John Jefferson, penthouse, Miss Jackson, likes suede jackets, jogs in the office; Vice-President Quincy Madison, Suite 36-N, Mrs. Pershing, likes fast sports cars, doesn't allow coffee breaks; Board Chairman Aaron Adams, Suite 35-S, Mr. Perry, likes cheese Danish, fears cars; Research Director James Burr, Suite 36-S, Miss Grant, likes long black cigars, donates to charities; Sales Manager Thomas Hancock, Suite 35-N, Miss Lee, likes bow ties, never wears a hat.

★ ★ ★ ★

97 $9,710,469 + 29,781,046 = 39,491,515$

★ ★ ★ ★

98 Darling Humpty: The King's horses and the King's men are coming in your direction. I have a nagging fear there could be a shocking accident. Do take care. Your loving Crumpety.

★ ★ ★ ★

NO POSTAGE
NECESSARY
IF MAILED
IN THE
UNITED STATES

BUSINESS REPLY MAIL
FIRST CLASS   PERMIT NO. 6484   DES MOINES, IOWA

POSTAGE WILL BE PAID BY ADDRESSEE

P.O. Box 10147
Des Moines, Iowa   50347-0147